Praise for *EATING LESS* by Gillian R

"Eating Less *is likely to succeed* simplicity *of its message and tech* continue *with a programme thai* eating and weight. *Gillian Riley exudes warmth and understanding of the problems of the compulsive dieter, and offers new hope by creating a shift in outlook and a method that confers responsibility and removes guilt.*

I will recommend it to anyone who is caught in the cycle of binge and deprivation - which causes misery by never addressing the underlying issue of coping with addictive behaviour."

Sarah Litvinoff,
psychologist and author,
The Relate Guide to Better Relationships

"Gillian places the emphasis where it belongs, on healthy eating and eating less, rather than seeing the problem as being overweight per se.

This book will be invaluable not only to people with an overeating problem but to those who are counselling them as well."

Joe Griffin,
psychotherapist and Director of Studies,
European Therapy Studies Institute

"I like the simplicity of the Eating Less *system; the basic principles are amazingly easy to understand and follow. Most importantly, I've lost many of my fears around the topic of food - fear of going out of control, fear of failure - and this gives me confidence that this is the permanent solution to my problem. I've found that I really can trust myself around food - even regaining my sense of humour about it all!"*

Mirjam Bollag Dondi,
psychotherapist,
Institute of Applied Psychology, Zurich

EATING LESS

Taking Control of Overeating

Gillian Riley

Published by

Gillian Riley
P. O. Box 2484
London
N6 5UX
England

ISBN 0 9534068 0 6

CONTENTS

"God gave me luck, health,
a voice and certain intelligence.
But if I could live my life over again,
there is one thing I would change.
I would want to be able to eat less."

Luciano Pavarotti

Reported in Time magazine
December 1997

1   A NEW LOOK

As you are no doubt aware, there is no shortage of books on the subjects of eating and weight loss. I read such books regularly, always looking to see if anybody else is working along the same lines as I am. The more I read, the more I see how different my approach really is.

Each of these books make their own unique contributions, but many contain similar themes, so I want to let you know right from the start that I'm not going to be repeating them. This is not to say that these ideas aren't valuable in many ways, it's just that they don't answer all of my questions. Perhaps they don't answer all of yours either.

Here are most of the main themes, and some of my thoughts about them:

- *Excess weight is not a health problem, so it's best to learn to love your body exactly as it is and accept yourself as a beautiful, heavier person.*

   I think it's a very good idea to love your body - but it's equally important to be honest about the fact that overeating does affect your health.

   An Expert Panel on Healthy Weight, appointed by the American Health Foundation in 1996, studied the research and concluded that for the best possible health, body mass index should be between 19 and 25. (Body mass index, or BMI, takes your height into account as well as your weight - see reference 1 to calculate yours). Risks for heart disease, high blood pressure, diabetes and many other diseases start to rise significantly with a BMI of 25 and above. (1)

   My purpose in writing *Eating Less* is to show you how to make changes, not to encourage you to settle for the way things are.

- *Overeating is the result of not dealing with your emotions. Learn to respond constructively to your true feelings, and you will no longer need to overeat.*

   If this is true, then why do people overeat when they're content, perhaps at a delightful dinner party? And why do people overeat even though they have become very skilled at dealing with their emotions - those who have been in therapy and therapists themselves, for example?

I can think of a number of people I know who overeat, and they deal with their emotions in positive and powerful ways. I can also think of people I know who are emotionally not at all on top of things, who do not overeat, or do drugs, drink or smoke. Perhaps you can think of people like this too.

It's true there is often a connection between negative emotional states and addictive behaviour of any kind - but this isn't the whole story.

- *Dieting makes you fat. Stop dieting and let your body find its natural weight.*
  We all know diets don't last, and, as we'll discuss later, dieting usually makes eating problems even worse in the long term. But what can you do instead? What you need is a way to control your overeating that is sustainable in the long term. Otherwise, even if you find your natural weight, you won't be able to maintain it. This book will show you how.

- *Eat only when you are genuinely hungry.*
  The main problem with this is that most people, especially those who overeat, find it extremely difficult to correctly identify genuine hunger. As an obese client of mine said recently: 'I don't think I'd recognise natural hunger if it jumped up and bit me on the nose.'
  Many people seem to feel hungry *after* eating a meal. In fact, it's quite possible you could conjure up some feelings of hunger almost any time at all. On the other hand, it is possible to go without eating for very long periods of time and still not feel any physical sensation of hunger. I experience this myself at times. I do not feel hungry, even though this makes no sense considering when and how much I last ate.
  Another problem with making hunger your cue to eat is simply that it can often be very inconvenient. If you are eating with others, in a restaurant for example, it seems silly to suggest that you delay your meal until you are sure your hunger has appeared. And it may not be practical to skip a meal at lunchtime because you're not hungry, only to find you are hungry an hour or two later - during a shift at work, in a meeting or when you need to pick up the kids from school.

It makes sense to aim for hunger as a sign to eat, but you will also need a guideline that's more tangible and is therefore less easily misinterpreted - and something that fits your own schedule!

- *Stop eating when you are full.*
It's even more difficult to be sure you've reached the right amount of fullness. Most people don't feel the 'fullness' of what they ate until about 10 minutes after finishing a meal. If you have a tendency to overeat, it's going to be too late by then. (2) Unfortunately, genuine body signals are often subtle and hard to read. Even when you are aware of them, you can very easily override them.

- *Addictive cravings are the result of biochemical imbalances and/or nutritional deficiencies.*
A common example of this theory is the idea that a craving for chocolate indicates the body's need for magnesium. The notion that our bodies give us signals telling us what we need to eat is very common, but, as we will see later, this is far from a complete explanation for addictive eating.
Here's a question to ponder: if I'm wanting to eat chocolate because my body needs magnesium, why don't I also crave green leafy vegetables such as kale, which contain even more of this mineral?

- *Abstinence from all 'binge' or 'trigger' foods must be maintained.*
According to one book that promotes this idea, abstinence must include all forms of: flour, sugar, chocolate, nuts, bananas, honey, bread, dried fruits, alcohol and caffeine - to name but a few from the list of 50 categories of addictive food.
I think it's true for most people that certain foods are more difficult to eat in a controlled way than others. But in the long term, abstinence from so many foods is burdensome, unrealistic and, most importantly, not at all necessary. A strategy for taking control will be more effective if it's attractive to you, if it's something you really do *want* to live with. And it needs to be flexible enough to suit you and your unique requirements and preferences, so that it's something you *can* live with.

- *Overeating is a rebellion against our culture's unrealistic expectations of what women should be and look like.*

  Cultural stereotypes of women and the pressure this creates can at best only partly explain overeating. If we compare the current figures for obesity in men and women in Britain, one in eight men and one in six women are considered to be obese (roughly 3 stone overweight). Yes, there is a difference between the sexes, but not a lot, and at least part of the difference could be due to the tendency of women's bodies to store fat more easily. One thing addicts tend to do a lot of is find something or someone else to blame for their problems, and often the easiest things to blame are those that are the most remote and intangible. The truth is you can take control of your eating in any cultural setting.

MIND CONTROL

So how can it be that I have something different to say on this well-worn topic? It's simply because I have been approaching the subject of overeating from a different perspective. That perspective is one of psychological addiction: the aspect of addiction that exists in the way we think.

I have been teaching people about addiction for the last 16 years. I have mainly focused on helping people to stop smoking, and achieve extremely high rates of success by explaining to smokers what psychological addiction is and how to deal with it. When this is understood, smokers are able not only to stop smoking, but stay stopped in the long term.

This is a crucial point, because many smokers find they can stop, but return to smoking later on because they haven't dealt with the psychological side of their addiction. In other words, they haven't changed the way they think about smoking.

In the same way, many overeaters are able to diet temporarily, but return to overeating because they haven't changed the way they think about eating.

Not only do my clients stop smoking, but many of them are pleasantly surprised to find they can do so without gaining any weight. This is because when they deal correctly with one addiction - smoking cigarettes - they don't need to replace it with another - eating food.

I have found, though, that there is a certain kind of smoker for whom smoking isn't really much of a problem at all. They are not really smokers, they are overeaters, and the only reason they ever smoke is because they don't know how else to control their addictive eating. The smoking part of stopping smoking is relatively easy for them. Their challenge is in facing up to their eating addiction.

Apart from smokers, I also work with people who want to make changes in their eating. These clients tell me it is extremely helpful to them to call overeating an addiction. When they start to handle their problem as an addiction they can begin to see things about their overeating that they had previously not seen, and as a result develop a degree of control they previously didn't have.

Finally, a confession. I eat - and I certainly have the ability to overeat. As a result, every word I write on this subject is tested by my personal experience. For me, this approach is all I'll ever use or need.

I strongly suspect I have as happy a relationship with food as anyone you'll ever meet. My weight fluctuates very little and I am in no sense at war with myself either with my shape or my food. I am keenly aware of my addictive thinking, and I believe it is nothing but this awareness that gives me the ability to be in control of my eating.

This is a book about taking control of addictive overeating. This is not a book about nutrition; there are already many excellent books available on the subject. This is not a book for people who are anorexic or bulimic, or those addicted to exercise, although it's possible they could benefit from reading it.

I've written this book for people who are overweight. Either a bit overweight or a lot overweight, or those who can't seem to get out of that cycle of dieting and regaining weight over and over again. This book is for people who have the same sorts of problems with food that other people have with cigarettes or other drugs.

If you've ever thought to yourself that you are addicted to food - this book is for you.

WHAT PEOPLE SAY ABOUT *EATING LESS*

"For the past fifteen years I had been struggling with what I eat, how I eat and what I weigh. I have tried numerous approaches: nutritionists, self-help groups, specific diets. Although some of these have helped, the sense of struggle I felt around eating had remained.

I was drawn to reading Eating Less and participating in the course because I knew about the success Gillian has had with helping people give up smoking. For me, eating is another addiction like smoking. To my mind, Eating Less offers something unique and ground-breaking.

For the first time in my life I now feel a sense of freedom around what I eat. I can apply a set of useful techniques, and my obsession with food is diminishing. Eating has become a natural process that I do at meal times without being fearful of how much I will eat, or wonder if I will be able to stop. The freedom I feel is such an enormous gift. My self esteem has risen, I feel more in control of my life and more confident."

DIANE

Taking Control

1. At the end of each chapter you'll find a section like this one, which highlights specific points raised in that chapter, suggests mental and written exercises, and changes for you to bring into your life. These exercises and suggestions will enable you to integrate this approach into your life so that you can make the changes you want to in your behaviour.

2. You may want to read this book on your own, or create a group to meet and discuss it on a regular basis. Or you may want to find a counsellor or therapist with whom you can explore the themes I describe.
   All of these are possibilities for you to choose from, depending on your own needs and circumstances. It's impossible to be too specific because each of us will have varying degrees of difficulty with these subjects.

3. My main advice at the start, as I advise each of my clients, is that you *don't make this technique the subject of general discussion with family and friends.* Your relationship with the food you eat is personal, private and unique to you; making a change in that relationship needs to be personal and private too. The people in your life may eat with you and even cook for you, but finally it's up to you and you alone what goes in your mouth.
   You might be tempted to explain what you've learned in this book in order to help others with their eating problems. *I strongly advise you against this* as it is likely to be met with resistance and could impair your own progress. If you want to, lend or give them a copy of this book - and then leave them alone to decide whether or not they want to read and use it.

2 YOUR PROBLEM ISN'T WEIGHT

People *can* change. *Everybody* can. In fact, all of us do change, simply because things happen to us as we go through our lives that inevitably make an impact and leave us different in some way. The question is not whether we change, but how much we passively drift into it and how much we direct change, choosing to create ourselves as the people we really want to be.

There are two crucial things to know about directing this kind of change. It never happens overnight, and it never gets done for you. Change takes time and it takes effort on your part. Right now, for example, you can't help but use your time and effort in order to read this.

However, when it comes to your weight - your body size and shape - it may well be that you've already spent considerable time and effort on making changes, but you've found the changes you tried to make either didn't work or didn't last. This, of course, can leave you doubting your ability to make the changes you want.

If what you tried before was some form of diet, then at least know you're not alone: according to a number of different surveys, of all the people who go on a diet, as many as 95% regain all the weight they lose. Maybe that's why you're reading this book. You are looking for something else.

Welcome to a completely different solution. This is not a diet book. This book is about making real, lasting change. The ideas I'll be introducing to you may not be easy to take on board and use immediately. This doesn't mean they aren't sound or that you are incapable of using them. It just means this is going to take time.

After all, it took you this long in your life to get to where you are now, so isn't it reasonable to take some time and effort to make effective changes? You may want an easy, instant cure, but is that really possible? What I hope to show you in these pages is that quick-fix solutions - diets, pills, magic slimming techniques - at best avoid the real problem, and can actually make it worse.

In fact, you may not even be seeing what the real problem is in the first place. The chances are you think your problem - what you want to *change* - is your weight. Ask yourself this: if your body size and shape was how you wanted it and it stayed that way, would you be reading this book? If you answer: 'Of course not!' then here's something for you to think about.

Weight is not your problem. It's one of the effects of your problem. Your problem is you eat more food than your body needs. Not more than somebody else's body needs. More than *your* body needs. Not more than your body used to need when you were younger or more active. More than your body needs now. Not more than your body would need if you had different genes and metabolism. More than your body needs with the genes and metabolism you have. That's why there's extra weight on it.

Saying the problem is 'eating' and not 'weight' might sound at first like I'm just playing with words, but let's think about it because it's very important.

The best way to understand this is by analogy. If you are overweight, this means you overeat, and this means you are, and probably feel, out of control when it comes to eating, at least sometimes. At times there is an addictive or compulsive quality to your eating.

This is similar to (but not exactly the same as) someone who is addictive or compulsive about smoking or drinking. The big difference is that the smoker and the drinker don't usually attempt to deal with their problem by trying to remove the *symptoms* of the problem.

Imagine a smoker who says: 'I'm coughing too much, what can I do to stop my coughing?' Someone points out that it's the smoking that's doing it, but the smoker says: 'Yes, I know, but all I really want is some good cough medicine'.

Imagine a drinker who says: 'My driving is terrible, I keep having accidents, where can I get some good driving lessons?' Someone suggests it's because he's driving drunk, so he keeps drinking and takes the bus.

Now, you may know that smokers and drinkers go through periods of time when they do think like this. It's called denial because they are denying the reality of what their problem actually is. The difference, though, is that when they finally admit they do have a problem, they tend to see it for what it is.

The point is that for eaters (as opposed to smokers and drinkers) this step is often not taken, or not taken fully. They still think in terms of trying to control their weight, which means keeping their sights set on an effect - not the cause, which is overeating.

It's a matter of balance, a matter of degree. *The more attached you are to losing weight, the more difficult it will be for you to stay in control of your overeating.* Let's start to look at why.

- When weight loss is all you care about, it makes sense to follow a diet. But whenever you go on a diet, it's inevitable you'll go off it sooner or later. A diet may help you to lose weight, but it's only a temporary solution to a permanent problem: your potential for overeating.

- When weight loss is all you care about, it's easier to ignore the nutritional value of the food you eat. You may not be giving your body the nutrition it needs, even eating things which do more harm than good, but when weight loss is your priority that's what influences your decisions.

- When weight loss is all you care about, you can end up feeling guilty about all your eating because all food contains calories. Especially after years of calorie-counting, your choices about what to eat can become harder to make because *any* choice to eat feels like a bad one.

- When weight loss is all you care about, you can end up doing things like passing on the beans and rice at dinner because they're 'fattening' but snacking on biscuits later that evening because you fancy them (…and after all, you've been so good all day, you skipped breakfast and you're going to the gym tomorrow so you'll work off the extra calories).

- When weight loss is all you care about, your results can be elusive and misleading. If you eat wisely and exercise, the lean muscle you gain will outweigh much of the fat you've lost. This means your weight doesn't change as much as your health and appearance does. It's very common to lose weight by losing lean tissue and water, without losing much fat at all. (1)

- When weight loss is all you care about, it's often hard to stay motivated because there will always be the days when, for various reasons, you just feel 'fat' no matter what you've been eating. Whether this is real or imagined, any sense of success can be so short-lived.

- When weight loss is your goal you never really achieve it, partly because it's never enough ('you can never be too rich or too thin') and partly because you fear you won't stay that way. It's such a fragile achievement.

- When weight loss is all you care about, it makes sense to employ strategies to avoid your compulsive desire to overeat. This has to be a temporary measure, and when the food-addict in you resurfaces the weight goes right back on - because dealing with your addictive eating was never your goal.

- When weight loss is all you care about, you avoid facing the reality of your addiction to food. After all, you're not addicted to weight: you don't get cravings late at night for 2lbs of fat to add to your thighs.

- When weight is all you care about, it's only when weight has gone back on that you start to think about taking some action. Then you are in that familiar - and unhealthy - cycle of weight loss and gain and loss and gain, known as yo-yo dieting or weight cycling.

- Most important of all, weight loss as a goal makes it easy to disregard the damage overeating does to your health, vitality and to your self-esteem - *in ways that have nothing to do with how you look.* We'll look at this in more detail later.

EATING LESS FOOD

Some people, of course, do give up their goal of losing weight *but they don't replace it with any other goals with regard to eating.* They just give up doing anything about any of it. You may identify with this, or it may be you *fear this is what will happen* if you let go of your attachment to weight loss as your principal goal.

The solution is to understand how else you will benefit from taking control of your overeating. One benefit will be weight loss, and, provided you are in fact overweight, there is nothing wrong with that at all. However, in order to do this, you need to make your body size less important to you and make taking control of your overeating your main goal. This requires a change in your thinking, a shifting of priorities.

At this point you might be thinking: 'Oh no, I really do want to deal with my eating problem', but ask yourself if it's still only a means to the same end. Ask yourself how much your purpose has to do with your weight, if you only want to control your overeating in order to be a certain size and shape. That's what I'm talking about.

Let me give you an illustration from real life. A woman phoned me up last week to inquire about coming to see me for help. She sounded very distressed, quite out of control of her eating and frantic about her weight. She wasn't sure whether to see me or join a Weight Watchers group much nearer to her home. 'I have a friend who has just lost 28lbs with Weight Watchers!' she screamed down the phone. 'She's a very old friend!' I wasn't sure if she saw this as more of a betrayal or a challenge, but either way she was extremely agitated about it and it was obvious that all she cared about was the weight loss. Later, I imagined her saying, with the same tone of fury in her voice: 'My friend has been eating a lot less food!'

That conversation, without any reference to weight, is very unlikely to happen - and yet this must be what the friend had done.

Here's another example of how people tend to think about this. When I first started writing this book I told many people I met that I was writing a book about addictive eating. Everybody who referred to it again referred to it as a book about losing weight. It's as if they had called my book on stopping smoking a book about improving lung capacity.

Placing the emphasis on 'taking control of your eating' enables us to get to grips with addiction. However, at first glance it could sound suspiciously like anorexia, as if you could end up having so much control over your eating that you hardly eat at all. In fact, eating too little is just as much a result of being out of control as eating too much. Part of what drives anorexia is such a fear of addictive eating that it seems the only safe thing is to eat almost nothing. After all, abstinence is the solution for most alcoholics and smokers. Unfortunately abstinence doesn't work so well with food! I use the phrase 'taking control of your eating' to include taking the best care of your health as you can. (2)

There are many different things that act together to create an eating problem. *One of the most significant is deciding to make your appearance more important to you than your health.* Anorexia and bulimia are extreme results of this, but it's relevant to us all to varying degrees. Our culture promotes placing the highest value on what others see, and we buy into it with our agreement. Look good at all costs. What matters is having the 'perfect' figure. What matters less, if at all, is becoming malnourished through our efforts to achieve it. Extra weight is judged, scorned and ridiculed almost everywhere, and it is precisely this that encourages us to attach ourselves so strongly and exclusively to the goal of weight loss.

Losing weight is a likely consequence of taking control of overeating. But when we are preoccupied with our appearance, which is a material concern, we pay less attention to the effects of addiction and what it costs us emotionally and spiritually to be out of control in such a significant area of our lives. And in many subtle and insidious ways we take less notice of the cost to our physical health as well.

The point is that while you are overeating, you are holding yourself back from becoming all you could be - in ways that have nothing to do with the size and shape of your body.

Of course, if you are like most addicts, you reason that when you have sorted yourself out and become all you can be (whatever that means to you) *then* you will be able to control your overeating. This is a case of putting the cart before the horse. The process of taking control of your overeating is a path - perhaps *the* path - towards a more confident, peaceful, happier and more fulfilled you. Making positive eating choices for the right reasons can lead you directly towards becoming the person you want to be and living your life the way you really want to live it.

I'm suggesting you prioritise a new goal: taking control of your overeating because that's your main source of physical and psychological well-being. Then, losing weight becomes a bonus.

Perhaps by now you are beginning to think: 'Yes, but what does it mean to be in control of my eating and how do I do it?' Great! This is a good question to be asking, and you are in the right place to get the answers because this is what this book is all about. Just understand that this is a very different question from: 'How do I lose weight?' *The first step in learning to control your overeating is to stop asking how you lose weight.*

I know this may seem to be a trivial distinction to make. It's easy to miss the significance of shifting your priority from what you weigh to what you eat, but look at it this way: if you are going on a hundred mile journey due south, and you turn a fraction to the left and take your journey slightly south-east, after a hundred miles you will end up in a very different place. Begin this hundred mile journey (it's actually a journey that will take you the rest of your life, as you are going to be eating for the rest of your life) by acknowledging that your best goal is to be in control of your eating.

Weight loss as a principal goal is fundamentally flawed. It addresses the effect not the cause of your problem, and only *one* effect at that. It's the one we can all see, but I want to suggest to you it's not really the most important one.

Being in control of your eating has far more significant implications for your life. And wanting to lose weight could be the one thing that keeps you from appreciating what these implications are, because when weight loss is all you care about, you invalidate these other, truly life-enhancing rewards. This is what we will look at further in our next two chapters.

WHAT PEOPLE SAY ABOUT EATING LESS

"I started to have eating problems roughly fifteen years ago. I sought help, but because I was not overweight, anorexic or bulimic, nobody would give me help.

I kept on eating junk food even though I had signs of poor health: unpleasant mood swings, PMS, fluid retention, fatigue, frequent nausea and abdominal bloating. I wanted to change but I thought there was no way out. Besides, most of the time I was denying the problem to myself, very much helped by the fact that it was never a weight problem, so I could conceal it.

Once I came to terms with the reality that I was addicted to food, a whole process of change began. I became engaged in a process of self-discovery that has gone far beyond the tangible consequences of overeating.

At first I experienced a huge resistance to change, yet the more I practice, the more I feel at ease with it and as a consequence with myself."

TULLIA

Taking Control

1. It takes deliberate and conscious effort to change your goal from wanting to lose weight to wanting to control your overeating. Whenever you think about your weight, think:

   'Weight is not my problem. Eating is'.

   This is true whether you are underweight, a bit overweight or a lot overweight. It could even be true if you are the weight you want to be.

   If you tend to be very concerned about your weight, it may not at first seem true to think of your problem as 'eating' rather than 'weight'. This requires a significant change in your thinking. I want to encourage you to stay with this, though, because you will find a breakthrough for yourself. Keep reviewing this book and take note of the ways in which changing this emphasis benefits you.

   By the way, when I refer to 'weight' I mean it to include the shape and the size of your body. 'Shape', 'size' and 'weight' all refer to the same thing: your appearance. They are different ways of describing *one* of the effects of your problem, not the cause, which is overeating.

2. If you normally weigh yourself, put your bathroom scales away. Unless you have a particular reason for knowing your weight, such as filling in an insurance form or for medical reasons, weigh yourself no more than once or twice a year, if that.

   When you weigh yourself over and over again you are using your weight to see whether you are succeeding or failing. In this book I will show you how to create a different standard of success or failure, one which relates to how much you are in control of your eating. In order to take on this new standard, you will need to let go of your old standard.

3. You may react to some things in later chapters by asking yourself: 'But how will that help me to lose weight?' Change the question to: 'How will that help me to take control of my eating?' and you will see the answer.

3 ALL THAT GLITTERS

Every day you make choices about food. You may be in a restaurant choosing from a menu, or in a supermarket choosing what to have for dinner that evening. Or you may be standing in your kitchen, trying to decide on a late night snack before bed. Every day, you choose when to eat, what to eat and how much to eat.

I'm assuming you're reading this book because in some way making these choices has become a problem for you. You eat things sometimes and later regret having done so. You make a plan not to eat certain kinds of foods but find you don't stick to it. You follow a diet for a while but sooner or later find yourself overeating again.

We will look at the details of when, what and how much to eat in later chapters. First, let's look at another factor involved in making a choice: the question of *why* you might choose either to eat or not to eat something.

Motivation (*why* am I doing this?) is crucial as it can make the difference between success and failure in anything you attempt to do. For example, if I asked you to give me £20, you would most likely want to know *why*. If I said that in return I'd give you a big smile, you probably wouldn't give me the money. But if I said that in return I'd give you a beautiful diamond ring, that's more likely to provide you with the motivation. In both cases, the action - giving me £20 - is the same. Without good motivation though, you may not choose to take the action.

When it comes to your choices about food (why am I eating/not eating this?) I want to suggest to you that at the heart of your motivation lies a very basic concept: self-esteem. Quite simply put, self-esteem is the opinion you have of yourself. It's impossible to have no opinion at all, and even though you may not spend much time thinking about what it is, this opinion does have a profound effect on your daily life. Just as the opinion you have of someone else affects every moment you spend with that person, so the opinion you have of yourself affects you.

A poor opinion means you experience low self-esteem, which can lead to persistent feelings of anxiety, insecurity and guilt, even when there's no good reason for these feelings. Positive opinions mean high self-esteem: confidence and ease with oneself, and an ability to accept mistakes and shortcomings as well as compliments and success.

It's natural to prefer to feel worthy and capable rather than inadequate and inferior, so when we try to make changes in our lives - going on a diet, for example - one of the main reasons we do it is in order to feel better about ourselves, to respect and honour ourselves a bit more. In other words, we do it in order to raise our self-esteem.

Now, when it comes to trying to feel better about ourselves, there's a big mistake a great many people make. The mistake is that we try to raise our self-esteem by gaining the approval of other people. We try to prove our worth to others so that we'll feel more worthy inside. And this is not just something we try on every now and then; it can become a significant part of daily life, our main motivation in doing almost anything at all.

It's not that other people's approval of you is a bad thing - it's just that it's the wrong place to look for self-esteem. The problem, you see, is that we can end up valuing the approval of others so much that our private achievements become utterly insignificant. Our own approval of ourselves can matter so little that we don't even stop to consider it. Often those people who esteem themselves the least are the very people most desperate to please others (or at least avoid their judgment and rejection, which is really the same thing). In the absence of genuine self-esteem, we try any way we can to 'prove' our value to somebody else.

We may try to impress others by owning more things or bigger and better things. Or we may seek approval by working harder, achieving more or by being more caring and helpful. And a great many of us try by looking better - which, of course, means thinner. *Wanting to own a better body can be just as much an attempt to gain self-esteem as is any other possession or achievement that's designed to impress others.*

I suspect that many people want to lose weight *primarily* in order that other people will approve of them more. Especially women, because that's what our culture expects of us, but I suspect this is relevant to a great many people, to a greater or lesser extent.

It is true, of course, that most people are more approving of a slimmer body. The problem is that when improving your appearance is your *main* - perhaps *only* - motivation behind your eating choices, you will tend to attach less significance to the private sources of *genuine* self-esteem: your own opinion of you, regardless of what others may think. *And it's the private sources of genuine self-esteem that provide you with much more effective motivation when it comes to taking control of an addiction.*

The truth for me is I do like to be admired by others for being slim - but I also know that there is danger in this way of thinking. It's dangerous because of what it does to my genuine self-esteem and therefore to my relationship with food, so it's a kind of motivation I don't deliberately encourage, either in myself or others.

Whether we consider ourselves to be overweight or not, our outward appearance, and what others may think of us because of it, often becomes *all that really matters.* Ask yourself these questions:

- Do you habitually compare your body size to others?
- Do you feel good about yourself if you turn out to be the slimmest in a group?
- Do you feel bad about yourself if you turn out to be the heaviest in a group?
- Do you form opinions about people based on how fat or slim they are?
- Are you more aware of the calorie content of food than the nutritional content?
- Have you ever thought to yourself: 'If only I was slim enough I'd be confident and happy - *I would esteem myself more*'?

It's an illusion a great many of us have bought, even those who have given up trying. And we've bought it quite literally in terms of the products sold to us which promote and (supposedly) deliver thinness as a commodity just like all the other commodities. This is why people literally stake their lives on slimming pills and crash diets, or risk anorexia and bulimia in their struggle for a sense of self-worth.

It will help you to remember that 'looking good' brings you *false* self-esteem - and that's a booby prize whether you win it or lose it. This is crucial, because this affects your daily life. Now. At least every time you eat.

You see, whenever you make a choice to eat or not to eat something, if your motivation in doing that has to do with weight, you are thinking in terms of *false* self-esteem. If you are thinking about eating a slice of chocolate cake, for example, and you think: 'I won't eat it because it's fattening' your motivation is in order to look more acceptable to other people.

However, if you think the solution is to say: 'I will eat it, even though I know it's fattening, because I don't care' you are still thinking in terms of your appearance to others. (The alternative, of course, is to think in terms of your own opinion of you, but we'll get to that later).

When your body size and shape is your main consideration in your choices about food, your main concern is other people's opinions or judgments of you.

Even if you have been advised to lose weight for health reasons, the chances are there is still a strong emotional attachment to your appearance which dominates your motivation. Maybe your doctor *said*: 'lose weight', but what you *heard* was: 'you don't look so good in that suit'. And maybe what your doctor really *meant* was: 'get your blood pressure down'

It could be that now you are thinking: 'But *I* like being slim, *I* enjoy it, it pleases *me*.' Yes, I know, I do too, but wanting to be slim may be more about other people's opinions of you than you realise:

- When you put on weight, isn't it when you think it's going to be noticed by other people that your heart sinks?
- When you lose weight, don't you want people to notice, even pointing it out to them if they don't make a comment?
- If you magically became your ideal weight right now, wouldn't you feel thrilled to look at yourself in a mirror? Don't mirrors show us what other people see?
- If you magically became your ideal weight right now, would you go to your next social event in the shapeless clothes you keep for when you're fat?

It's been so overemphasised in our culture, it's almost impossible not to be affected by it - especially for women. Think of every film you ever saw, where the skinniest, tiniest women are the central, most interesting characters. Look at any mannequin in any dress shop window. Look at all our 'beautiful' fashion models who live dangerously close to starvation. Does this make any sense?

It makes sense if you are in the business of selling false self-esteem. Then it makes very good sense, because there is no shortage of buyers.

Losing weight usually creates a 'high' from false esteem, in the same way as buying a flashy car or wearing the latest fashion. That high can be powerful and *very* seductive, but inside, nothing's changed and you probably know it. Nothing can fool the truth inside your own heart, and in your own heart you know that having a more impressive body does nothing to improve your genuine self-esteem.

It may be you have already figured this out and stopped trying to lose weight. You may be well aware that the image you present to the world does little to improve the image you have of yourself. And of course you may genuinely esteem yourself in ways that have nothing to do with your weight or your eating.

But still, you may have missed a very exciting opportunity. This is the opportunity to make changes in your eating, not to impress others, but to increase your own capacity to live your life to the full. Not so much because you *look* your best, but because you *feel* your best - because you have higher *genuine* self-esteem.

You could regard your choices about eating as the way you raise your genuine self-esteem. So the way you motivate yourself to eat or not to eat something isn't primarily about how you appear to others, it's primarily about how you feel about yourself. If you do that, you may benefit in more ways than you can imagine.

PRIORITISING SELF-ESTEEM

If you are someone who tends to have low self-esteem, you might now be thinking: 'If only I felt better about myself, then I would be able to make changes in my eating'. However, I know that people with low self-esteem can make huge changes - and gain self-esteem as a result. I know this because I have seen so many of my clients go through this process. You may struggle initially because you're so convinced you'll fail, but it's exactly in the facing of this fear that strength and confidence in yourself will arise.

Another concern you could have is an objection to the idea of raising your level of self-esteem at all. Many people make the mistake of thinking that high self-esteem is an arrogant, inflated opinion of oneself and indifference to others. This is *not* self-esteem; in fact it is a *lack* of genuine self-esteem that leads people to become so self-centred. Wanting to feel superior is just another false esteem fix.

Yet another possibility is that you are someone who tends to have high self-esteem already, who rarely feels any need to prove their worth to others. This is a good place to start from, but don't let this fool you into thinking you won't benefit from taking control of overeating.

I find the words 'inner joy' helpful in describing genuine self-esteem. Can you honestly say you wouldn't want more of that? It doesn't mean you will never make mistakes. It means you won't feel quite so crushed when you do. It doesn't mean you'll feel instantly confident in facing new challenges. It does mean you're more likely to appreciate both the challenge and yourself for facing it. Most of all, it doesn't rely on other people applauding your achievements. That's nice when it happens, but it's not essential.

Genuine self-esteem comes from inside you; *it's very private.* This means you improve it at the same time as you let go of some of the significance of other people's opinions of you. Make your self-esteem more important to you and your weight less important. Then, you are prioritising your opinions of you, rather than other people's.

Your appearance - your body shape and size - will no doubt always be significant to you, as mine is to me. What I'm talking about here is putting it into a different perspective. The more you concern yourself with improving your own opinion of you, regardless of your weight, the more you will be able to stay in touch with motivation *that really works.* (1)

Of course, this still leaves the question of how you do go about improving your genuine self-esteem, so in our next chapter we'll see what a leading authority on self-esteem has to say. This is just one view of many, and I present you with this approach because it works for me, especially when it comes to taking control of overeating. My suggestion is to try it and see if it works for you.

WHAT PEOPLE SAY ABOUT *EATING LESS*

"I had always been a couple of stone overweight, a size too big. A couple of years ago I successfully dieted to my target weight and looked and felt great. But it seemed a very brittle kind of success and the weight had crept back on over the last two years or so.

I don't think people who have never had a weight problem understand the state of mind that goes with it. I would describe myself as confident, outgoing and successful but I have always felt that I wasn't quite as good as everyone else, and attributed it to being fat. I have felt this way since I was a teenager. Yet even having dieted successfully, that feeling didn't go away.

One of the most important things I learned on the Eating Less course was how weight is a red herring; the damage to your self-esteem is done by the overeating, not by being overweight."

SARAH

Taking Control

1. It's helpful to realise that low self-esteem is often behind the low moods you might call: 'having a bad day', 'feeling negative' or 'hating my life'. At times like this you may tend to think: 'if only I was slimmer, all my problems would disappear'. Raising your self-esteem may not make *all* your problems disappear - but it will come a lot closer to it than losing weight will!

   Whenever you think about your weight, consider this: 'what I weigh is not important - what's important is how I feel about myself, regardless of my size and shape'. Another way to put this is: 'having control of my overeating is more important to me than looking more acceptable to others'.

2. Any time you lose weight, don't mention it to anyone.

3. If you are getting support with your eating issues from a group or a counsellor resist mentioning, discussing, acknowledging and especially applauding weight loss.

4. If you are one of those people who compares their body size and shape to others, the next time you notice yourself doing this, remind yourself that your self-esteem has *nothing* to do with the size of someone else's body.

5. Whenever you eat in an addictive way, be brave enough to do it in front of other people just as much as you do it on your own. This will help you to lessen the significance of other people's opinions of you when it comes to your relationship with food.

   It's not that other people's opinions aren't important, it's just that it damages your own self-esteem if you make their opinions of you more important than your own.

4 MOTIVATION THAT WORKS

Dr Nathaniel Branden is a psychologist and author who has been studying and writing about the significance of self-esteem for about 40 years. To date he has written 16 books on the subject, many of which are best-sellers and published in many parts of the world, including the USA, Europe, Brazil and China.

In *The Six Pillars of Self-Esteem* he describes the six principles on which self-esteem depends:

- living consciously
- self-responsibility
- living purposefully
- self-acceptance
- self-assertiveness
- personal integrity

These are not just ideas, they are ways to live. Not as ideal states of perfection - that is unrealistic - but as directions to aim towards. The point is, the more you live by these principles, the higher your self-esteem will be.

The very interesting thing for us and our relationship with food is that it is exactly the practice of these six principles that gives us the ability to take control of addictive eating. In fact, I can't think of one thing we need to do in order to take control of an addiction that isn't included in that list. So, when we apply these principles to our addictive behaviour, we take control *and* we raise our genuine self-esteem at the same time.

LIVING CONSCIOUSLY – Although nobody can be conscious of everything all the time, in general, the more aware you are the greater your ability to change your behaviour. As a simple example, if you wanted to cut down on sugar you would do better if you were aware of which foods contained sugar.

Do you know that the word 'curiosity' comes from the same root as the word 'cure'? Your curiosity leads you to your cure. It's doing it right now! It's not sufficient, however, simply to *be* curious; *living* consciously implies that what you discover gets put into practice.

Many aspects of addictive behaviour become automatic and therefore out of our range of awareness. Each chapter in this book will help you to understand more about addiction, and will therefore bring you greater ability to take conscious control - and as a result, raise your self-esteem.

SELF-ACCEPTANCE – Self-acceptance *doesn't* mean you think everything's perfect just as it is. What it means is that you be your own friend in this, not your enemy. Even though you dislike many things about overeating, have some compassion for the human being who is caught up in it. It's recognising your inherent worth as a human being - *regardless of anything you do and regardless of what you look like* - that inspires you to create a way of life that reflects and honours your inherent worth.

Self-acceptance also means getting yourself to accept that things are the way they are. Accept the fact that, at least sometimes, you eat in an addictive way. Accept the fact that it's impossible for you to continue to eat that way and maintain the best possible state of health. Accept these as facts of reality, no matter how much you may not like them.

SELF-RESPONSIBILITY – Of these six principles, self-responsibility is likely to be the most misunderstood, especially when it comes to taking control of overeating. I suspect you may regard the notion as a dreary prospect, and the last thing you'd want to do!

In fact, taking responsibility gives you an extraordinary degree of control over your addictive eating because it brings you the freedom to choose - something that is compromised by addiction. *Taking responsibility is a step towards freedom, not away from it.* Chapter Six will explain much more about this and how you can put it into practice.

Whatever you've achieved in your life, it's because you took responsibility for it. Perhaps you can think of something else you've accomplished simply because you stopped waiting for someone else to come along and do it for you. Remember the effect this had on your self-esteem.

SELF-ASSERTIVENESS – Self-assertiveness is relevant when you eat with others. A key for you may be in making your own choices, at least sometimes, instead of always eating what other people want you to eat or always eating certain kinds of things simply because other people are eating them.

You may need to assert yourself by explaining some things to people who push you to eat when it's really not right for you to do so. Or you may want to have a talk with the person who shops and cooks for you, in order to make clear agreements about what you want to eat.

LIVING PURPOSEFULLY – When we live purposefully we set goals and then work towards them. We'll get to what your goals about food could be later on. They won't be about weight loss; they will be about taking control of addictive eating. As you read on you will see how to put that into practice.

PERSONAL INTEGRITY – If another person lied to you, made you do things you later regretted or damaged your health, I imagine you wouldn't hold them in very high esteem. When it comes to food, you may have been doing this to yourself in many ways for a long time. Even if you just do it less often, your sense of personal integrity will soar and so will your self-esteem. It simply means doing what you believe in, doing what you say you will do and telling the truth to yourself.

When it comes to food, do not put up with lies - or even 'white-lies'. Addictive behaviour is always maintained by deceptions of various kinds. Telling the truth is your way out.

These six principles may well be familiar to you, and not only in connection with eating. And it may well be that you have practised these principles and enjoyed the benefits of healthier self-esteem when you've been in control of your eating in the past. So you know what I'm talking about here in your own experience.

But it may also be that you tended to invalidate these rewards because you prioritised your body shape and size, perhaps to the exclusion of everything else. The value in declaring your self-esteem as your main motivation behind your choices about eating is that you make the whole process more deliberate, and therefore more powerful and effective.

You see, *whether you recognise it or not*, every time you make a choice about eating you make a choice that has an effect on your self-esteem. With a single choice the effect may be quite subtle, but the extraordinary thing about food is that you encounter it all the time, so you affect your self-esteem all the time. The effect is cumulative.

Dr. Branden's view is that high self-esteem is something you can *achieve*. What I'm saying is that the issue of what and how much you eat provides you with a unique and extraordinary opportunity to achieve higher self-esteem. It's true your self-esteem is affected by all aspects of your life, but food has a very special significance. Not only is food a regular part of your daily life - it's fundamental and essential to your life. Your food becomes you - so the way you are with your food leaves a more profound impression on your self-esteem than almost anything else.

YOUR REWARDS

Finding out that you determine how much you esteem yourself, that you have an enormous impact on your self-esteem on a daily basis, may at first seem both liberating and frightening. Many people believe that self-esteem is an inevitable consequence of childhood; that if they were invalidated by parents and teachers when they were young, they must resign themselves to low self-esteem for life. You may criticise yourself a great deal and live with a sense that whatever you do, it's never enough - and it's true this probably has its roots in your past.

With patience and persistence, it is possible for you to change this script. The only thing that could prevent you is your fear of the very changes you want to make. Your fear of change may sound familiar: 'Oh, but this is me - it's just how I am!' Remember to go as slow or as fast as you want; you are not in a race. Get support for yourself if you want to. You have the rest of your life to work on this, and even small steps can produce exciting results.

Not only does your relationship with food improve, but by taking on these principles with regard to food, you increase their significance in your life. So in taking control of your overeating you take more control of your life in general. By becoming more at peace with your eating you will become more at peace with yourself. In gaining a healthy relationship with food you will improve your relationships with everyone in your life - especially yourself.

And for a great many people, raising your self-esteem will be the only way you can make 'looking good' lose some of its significance.

You may have believed for much of your life that your worth as a human being is determined by the size of your body, and you'll find that things really start to change when you to give up trying to prove your self-worth in this way. Since it doesn't generate genuine self-esteem anyway, *it's never enough*, even when you do receive some kind of approval from someone else.

This is an arena that provides you with opportunities like no other. Begin by treating yourself as if you are more worthy, regardless of your size, and before too long you will feel more worthy, regardless of your size. Simply pay attention to all the ways your life improves when you are in control of your eating:

BENEFITS YOU GAIN FROM RAISING YOUR LEVEL OF SELF-ESTEEM

- inner strength and confidence, rather than feeling like a victim of life
- inner joy and peace, which is less dependent on external circumstances
- feeling more at ease with yourself, either when you're alone or with others
- feeling grounded and centred
- productivity and enthusiasm for life
- less dependent and therefore more satisfying relationships
- greater ability to trust yourself and your own thinking
- creativity, because you believe in yourself more
- less sensitivity to criticism
- less self-conscious and anxious
- less need to be defensive, competitive or judgmental
- greater ability to recover from other compulsive behaviours such as smoking or working
- greater ability to cope with major life changes, such as death of relative, end of relationship, redundancy or retirement

BENEFITS YOU GAIN FROM TAKING CONTROL OF YOUR EATING, BESIDES HIGHER SELF-ESTEEM AND WEIGHT LOSS

- you take control of your life, instead of being controlled by your addictive appetite
- greater enjoyment of eating, free from guilt
- vitality and energy, feeling more alive
- social life free from preoccupation with food

- freedom from bloated, uncomfortable feelings from eating too much
- freedom from diets
- freedom to cook anything for others, knowing you don't have to eat it
- ability to think more clearly
- savings in money and time
- more adaptable to seasonal temperature changes
- less susceptible to stress
- better health...

I was going to attempt a list of physical ailments connected with addictive eating, but I can't think of many health problems that *aren't* affected by the food we eat. It's crucial for you to acknowledge that the ongoing maladies you may suffer from - such things as fatigue, various infections, constipation, diarrhoea, haemorrhoids, premenstrual tension, stomach aches and clogged sinuses - are in almost all cases preventable and treatable by the quality and quantity of the food you eat. Even serious conditions such as high blood pressure, diabetes (non-insulin dependent), heart disease, strokes, arthritis and cancer are often directly linked with addictive eating. (1)

Many people believe illnesses such as these are determined by the luck of their genes, and it is true that we do tend to inherit the same genetic 'Achilles heel' as other members of our family. What this means, though, is that overeating in one family usually leads to diabetes, while in another family overeating usually leads to heart disease or a particular kind of cancer. In another, arthritis, and so on.

By taking control of your overeating you will at the very least delay the onset of conditions such as these, and you could avoid them all together. There are many factors that work together to create illness: stress, genes, inactivity, environment - and certainly our minds and emotions play no small part. But food is also a very significant factor - and as a food addict this may well be the very last thing you want to acknowledge.

If you think we have strayed off the subject of self-esteem here, we have not. Placing value on your physical health - whether as a healing or preventative measure - strengthens your self-esteem, just as eating in a way that could harm your health undermines it.

Even after all this, I suspect I still haven't fully convinced you. I am well aware of the allure of 'looking good'. If you think you could look like a film star, and I'm just offering you self-esteem, what are you most likely to use to motivate yourself? It can still turn into: 'Ok, ok, I'll go for the self-esteem if you think that will help me to lose weight'!

The attraction of weight loss as your main goal can be even stronger if you are very overweight. You may not want to look like a star, just a 'normal' person who doesn't get rude stares everywhere they go. Even so, prioritising weight loss can lead you off track.

You might lose some weight, but the chances are you will sabotage yourself in some way if your self-esteem remains low. People who dislike themselves often feel compelled to punish themselves by doing things they know they will regret later on. Then this self-destructive behaviour lowers self-esteem even more. You may be all too familiar with: 'I'm fat, so I'm worthless, so I might as well eat more, so I overeat, then I feel guilty, and I get fatter, which proves I'm worthless, so I might as well eat...'

This vicious circle is driven by exaggerated, inappropriate guilt: the hallmark of low self-esteem. In the past you may have tried to break this cycle by trying to lose weight. *But if you measure your worth by your body size, it may be a long time before you feel any better about yourself, so it's easy to return to overeating.*

You can apply the practice of the 'six pillars' - living consciously, self-acceptance, self-responsibility, self-assertiveness, living purposefully and personal integrity - specifically with regard to food, whatever your appearance. *Then you break the cycle by raising your self-esteem.* Don't just take my word for it; apply these six principles to your eating - you'll see how to do this as you read on - and you will experience your self-esteem improve long before you achieve any significant weight loss.

In order to do this, though, you need to start out by prioritising motivation that is about anything other than your weight, shape and size. *Look for any reason to make changes in your eating other than your appearance.*

In my experience, when I keep in mind the impact my eating has on my self-esteem, I don't overeat because I know the rewards of not doing so are precious to me. The best way to describe it is I become significantly happier, regardless of external circumstances in my life. I can't think of anything else that has as much impact on my self-esteem as my eating. No, not my weight. My *eating*.

That's what works for me. Just try it, and see if it works for you. If it doesn't, you can discard it. It doesn't have to be a permanent commitment.

It's crucial that you take control of your addictive eating because *you* are going to get something *you* really want out of it. You see, whether it's drinking, smoking, overeating or whatever, the most compelling aspect of any addiction is that you are doing it because it brings you pleasure. If you try to limit this pleasure in order to please or impress others it becomes an act of self-sacrifice - and it's very difficult to stay motivated to keep sacrificing yourself. Not only that, but your motivation is dependent on how those others are treating you. Any time they let you down, the thing to do *for yourself* will be to eat. *You see, you will need to find more pleasure in controlling your eating than in overeating - otherwise you won't stay with it.* We are going to start looking at addiction in our next chapter.

WHAT PEOPLE SAY ABOUT *EATING LESS*

"I'm eating about half the amount I used to before I did the Eating Less course. My digestive problems seem to have sorted themselves out. I used to suffer with heartburn and feelings of nausea almost every time I ate, and these have pretty much disappeared, mainly, I think, from eating a lot less fat. Also, not eating as often. I used to eat every two hours, and now I feel better eating after at least four hours.

I have a more positive attitude in general and a lot more energy; it's like a stress has been lifted. It's a mental state that has changed. I'm not depressed about my eating any more and I don't feel so helpless. I had resigned myself to getting heavier and heavier and never being able to do anything about it. All kinds of social events are a lot less stressful now because I don't feel desperate about being at parties and stuffing myself with food."

MARGARET

Taking Control

1. Write a list or letter to yourself with as much detail as you can about what it means to you to be in control of your eating and what it costs you to be out of control. Put the emphasis on eating rather than weight. If you have been in the habit of ignoring or invalidating these less concrete benefits, you may need to spend some time thinking about what this means to you.

   Keep the list or letter somewhere safe, private and easily accessible, like a filofax, a diary or a jewellery box. Add to it as you go along.

2. Don't tell other people about your triumphs and successes in taking control of your overeating. By keeping this to yourself you begin to break down some of your dependency on other people's approval. Get used to feeling your pride in your accomplishments, acknowledging the effect on your own self-esteem - *privately.*

3. When you do lose some weight, it's inevitable and very understandable that you'll feel delighted. However, it will help you to resist wearing clothes that emphasise and show off your new shape and size, at least for a while. Remind yourself of all you are achieving in areas other than body size. If you ignore this advice you could be making things harder for yourself, and your addictive eating may increase.

   I'm not suggesting you should never wear smaller sizes. I'm suggesting you take things very slowly. Changing your body shape is a big thing to do. Ease into it gradually, make it as insignificant as you possibly can, and it's much more likely to last.

5   WHAT IS AN ADDICTION?

I'm aware that up to now I've been using the word 'addiction' without saying very much about what addiction is. In this chapter we'll start to look at what an addiction is made of, so we can then understand better how to deal with it.

Not everybody agrees that food is addictive. Some people flatly deny it, usually because they define addiction purely in terms of physical dependency on drugs.

My conviction that people do become addicted to food has come from my experience of helping people to stop smoking. Smokers frequently smoke instead of eat, and, especially when stopping smoking, eat instead of smoke. Tobacco is widely accepted as being addictive, and for many people the impulse to smoke and the impulse to eat become interchangeable and even at times indistinguishable. By saying food is addictive we don't create a problem, but face an existing one with the truth.

Even so, calling food an addiction raises many more questions than it answers. First, let's look at a list of things people usually think of as being addictive:

alcohol, nicotine, heroin, methadone, cocaine, cannabis, solvents, caffeine, tranquillisers, amphetamines, exercise, television, computer games, computers, working, gambling, sex, shopping - and food, especially processed foods containing refined sugar, refined flour, fats and/or salt.

This isn't a complete list, but it's enough for us to begin to get a picture. Each one, of course, has its own particular characteristics. Food addiction is not the same as gambling addiction. Being a smoker is not the same as being a compulsive shopper. What's important are the characteristics they share that cause them to be called addictions, at least sometimes for some people. Let's see what those characteristics are and how they show up with food.

I WANT IT (addictive desire) – Perhaps the most obvious characteristic of addiction is a concept so familiar we have many words to describe it: desire, craving, compulsion, urge, yearning, longing, anticipation and even obsession. When you are addicted to something, you want to do whatever it is you are addicted to. You are somehow attracted to it.

It is this desire that makes the behaviour difficult to control, why there's a tendency to relapse. This is implicit in the idea of addiction: it's something you have difficulty not doing because at the same time as wanting to stop doing it, you are also wanting to do it!

The addictive desire is a 'conditioned response', which means you automatically associate your addiction with certain cues. For example, if I eat popcorn every time I go to the cinema, I condition myself to expect popcorn whenever I go to the cinema. My memory produces the conditioned response - the addictive desire - whether or not I'm naturally hungry.

The conditioned response is a major factor in all addictions, but it's especially important in dealing with smoking and eating because the cues are so thoroughly integrated into so much of our daily lives.

IT's BAD FOR ME (cost) – When we call something an addiction we imply there's a problem of some kind. There's a cost in continuing to satisfy our addictive desire, in terms of health, wealth and self-esteem. We may be addicted to things that are good for us, such as food or exercise, but the part of the behaviour we call 'addiction' is, *by definition*, the part that is detrimental in some way.

Addictions never contribute to our well-being. Essentials such as sleeping, although repeated daily all through our lives, aren't called addictions. We genuinely need to sleep, so there's no problem. In fact, we have problems if we don't do it.

Sooner or later the cost of the addiction may get too high and the addict starts trying to control the behaviour. When addictive behaviour continues in spite of the cost, guilt becomes an added problem.

The cost isn't just the 'downside', it actually adds power to the addiction, making it more attractive. The danger and illegality of drugs make them more interesting for some people than they would otherwise be. Food addiction may look innocent, but the same mechanism is at work: it becomes 'naughty fun' if it's forbidden in some way.

Extra weight is usually the most obvious cost of food addiction, but, as I hope I've established in preceding chapters, it will serve you to become aware of the other things you inevitably sacrifice in the pursuit of your 'fix'.

I LOVE IT (pleasure) – The satisfaction of our addictive desire usually brings us pleasure, and, of course, pleasure is very much a matter of personal preference. For example, I can't think of much that's less pleasurable than gambling - but there may well be compulsive gamblers who are indifferent to chocolate-covered raisins.

Addiction lives in the world of sensation, often supported by a hedonistic view of life: that the pursuit of pleasure is the highest good. It's fuelled by a sense of excitement, satisfaction or reward. This is why we have the addictive desire: we tend to want to repeat doing things which we enjoy.

There can come a time when an addict derives no pleasure from their addiction because the cost has become too overwhelming, but at some time in the development of the addiction, pleasure was involved.

[This distinguishes addiction from 'obsessive-compulsive disorder' (OCD). An example of OCD is compulsive hand-washing, and the main reason this is not thought of as addiction is there's no pleasure involved at any point. The person with OCD doesn't think: 'I can't wait to get home and get some of that lovely sandalwood soap all over my hands.']

When it comes to dealing with food addiction, one difficulty is that pleasure and satisfaction are perfectly normal, appropriate and even necessary responses to eating food. This gives credibility to the familiar justification for overeating: 'I enjoy my food - what's wrong with that?' *Our challenge is to recognise the difference between appropriate enjoyment and the satisfaction of addictive desire.*

IT MAKES ME HAPPY (altered state of consciousness) – To varying degrees, addictions temporarily change the way we are thinking and feeling; they make us high, drugged, 'absent-minded' or numbed in some way. Overeaters can go into a kind of daze even while eating a perfectly ordinary meal. A food binge can create a state of intoxication not unlike that produced by alcohol.

This altered state of consciousness can create a buffer between us and our feelings, and this brings us a sense of comfort, which is why we often turn to our addictions when we are unhappy or stressed. A number of books on overeating focus on this exclusively as the cause of overeating, but you can probably tell from your own experience that you do eat addictively even when you are perfectly happy. Satisfying our addictive desire usually brings us pleasure and comfort, so there aren't many circumstances in which we will not want to do that.

I LOVE EVERYTHING ABOUT IT (secondary conditioning) – Not only do we get pleasure from the addiction, but also from all kinds of things directly associated with it. Heroin addicts can get as much excitement from procuring their drug and preparing it for use as in doing it. Some alcoholics thoroughly enjoy their active social life only because it's integral to their drinking; without the booze the friends would be worthless.

In the same way, shopping for food, preparation of food and social events which include eating carry a special significance for the addicted eater. Food could be your hobby and even your career.

Again, the difficulty with food addiction is that it all seems so completely *natural*. It's important, though, to see what this addiction is made of, and that it's made up of the same things as other addictions.

I FEEL IT IN MY BODY (interaction of body and mind) – Many people believe that addictive behaviour is caused by body chemistry. An addictive desire to eat is often experienced as a physical feeling so it's easily to assume that if it's felt in the body, it's created in the body - but this isn't necessarily the case. A great many physical sensations arise from states of mind: emotions such as anger and disappointment, stage fright and panic attacks, to name but a few examples. (1)

I'M PRONE TO IT (susceptibility) – Everybody's body is different. We aren't all born with the potential to become world-class athletes, opera singers - or alcoholics. All we can work with is what we've been given.

What we *may* have been given is a predisposition to become addicted to things in general, and we *may* have been given a predisposition to become addicted to food. Research is not conclusive on this, but as an example, a Stanford University study showed that a quarter of an otherwise normal, healthy population produce too much insulin in response to carbohydrates. (2)

This could be a physical factor in addictive eating - but remember it's just one part of the whole picture. It doesn't mean you'll never be able to make lasting changes.

EVERYONE ELSE IS DOING IT (exposure) – Before we can take up a particular addiction we must have access to it, and the more widespread it is in our community, the more likely we are to get involved. If all my friends smoke I am more likely to join in - especially if I'm young.

Of course most of us have access to too much food and poor quality food, but some social groups encourage its consumption. You may be part of a family or group of friends that takes addictive eating for granted, perhaps even regarding it as healthy, for example, when people say: 'He's got a healthy appetite'.

This doesn't mean you can't do anything about your own eating - just don't try to change theirs! What may be required is for you to assert yourself, saying: 'no thanks' instead of conforming to peer pressure. When you do respond in that way, notice the effect this has on your self-esteem.

The culture we live in is one that encourages addictive eating. Our food industry is chiefly concerned with marketing its products, which usually means promoting the more addictive foods - processed products containing fats, sugar, flour and salt - rather than health. 'Health' may be a good marketing strategy, but is rarely, if ever, much more than that.

Advertising and availability make addictive junk food seem 'normal'. As a result a great many of us have become confused about food, unable to appreciate or even care about the essential difference between a bag of crisps and an apple, for example. (3)

Just because something is considered acceptable within a culture or group, doesn't mean it isn't addictive behaviour. In many parts of the world it is considered normal to smoke, and so many people smoke it's considered odd if you don't. This doesn't mean the smokers are not addicted, it just means that this particular society has a different attitude towards this addiction.

Your social group may consider it normal to eat a portion of chips every day for lunch. Your family may think it perfectly normal to eat a sweet and fatty pudding after every meal. I was raised in such a family. This doesn't mean it isn't addictive eating, just because everybody around you is doing it.

There's another kind of peer pressure you might be exposed to, and that is endless conversations about weight and dieting. If you have a friend or group of friends with whom you discuss these issues, I want to suggest to you that this is part of your addiction, and it might be a good idea for you start to think of ways to remove yourself from these conversations.

IT'S UNCOMFORTABLE WHEN I STOP (withdrawal symptoms) – Withdrawal symptoms are anything negative, difficult or unpleasant that happen as a result of stopping the addictive behaviour. Symptoms are often thought of as purely physical, but there is also a mental side to withdrawal, which is really much more significant.

The physical side can look like illness, but it's just recovery from the abuse of the addiction. With food, health and nutrition expert Leslie Kenton speaks of 'cleansing-reactions' to a detoxification diet in her '10 Day Clean-Up Plan':

'Such reactions can include headaches, muscle or joint pains, sensitivity, tiredness... due to the rapid mobilisation and release of stored toxins and wastes. (Your body) is working very hard to clean and renew itself...'

It's possible, though, that we don't have to do a detox diet to experience withdrawal symptoms from food. It could be that a whole range of ailments are really withdrawal symptoms from whatever addictive junk food we consumed the previous day. We may regard our aches, low energy and inability to concentrate as permanent and inevitable features in our lives, only seeing their connection with food when we make changes in our eating.

Far more important for us, though, are the *mental* changes involved in withdrawing from food addiction. There is much in this book about changing the way you think. If you find it thought-provoking, even shocking or alarming, and if you spend a lot of time thinking about it, I would call that being in mental withdrawal.

Mental withdrawal is the difficulty in making a real change, and as such it's an essential part of the process. Taking control of overeating, as any other addiction, is a major change to be making.

You don't go through something like that without some kind of inner struggle.

I'M USED TO IT (tolerance) – This refers to our ability to adapt to and endure the abuse we may inflict on our bodies. For example, we could take small amounts of poison, gradually increase the dose and eventually survive what would otherwise be a fatal dose. Tolerance means we get used to unnatural substances, which is why doses usually increase.

For example, people may start smoking only one or two cigarettes a day, but over time increase that to 20 or 30 a day. The body becomes tolerant of the drug and more of it is required in order to achieve the same effect. If a non-smoker tried to smoke 30 in a day, they would feel dreadful because they haven't built up the tolerance.

With food addiction, our stomachs expand so we can tolerate larger amounts. We also develop tolerance for the quality of food. People often say their taste-buds change after making changes in what they eat. Extremes of sugar and fat, for example, don't appeal as much as they once did because their tolerance for them has faded.

I COULDN'T COPE WITHOUT IT (justification) and *WHAT'S WRONG WITH IT ANYWAY* (denial) – All addictions are supported by ways of thinking that become so familiar it can be tough to separate the truth in them from the illusion. These beliefs work hand in hand to *justify* satisfying the addictive desire and to *deny* a) that you're eating addictively in the first place, and b) even if you are, that it's bad for you in any way.

Justification and denial are such a powerful part of addiction, it's essential to break their hold by rigorous truth-telling. After all, if your life will fall apart without the addiction, and it isn't doing you any harm, why would you ever stop doing it?

Justification and denial are attempts to feel OK about the addiction. Whenever the denial is challenged - when you get ill for example - the more you realise the addiction is really *not* OK, the more you'll rely on your justifications, so the more convincing they will need to be. This tends to create some fear at the thought of taking control of the addiction, because you believe you are dependent on it in some significant way.

This doesn't mean the justifications and the fear they create are your best guides to your wisest decisions. Facing the fear is always going to be part of the process because it's only by facing fear that you can overcome it. We'll look at justifications in more detail in Chapters Nine and Ten.

As an example of denial, I remember one client in particular, Janet, who swore to me she couldn't think of one reason to cut back on her overeating other than her weight. She thought and thought, and looked at me as if I was mad to suggest such a silly idea. But only two weeks before she had cancelled a session with me because of a migraine which she had told me was brought on by the overeating she had done the day before. Her addicted mind had simply blanked this out.

Denial is tricky to overcome because the whole point of it is that it's hidden from you. It's safe to assume, though, that there is some denial going on with any addictive behaviour. (4)

Take note of any physical symptoms of ill health you may have, especially persistent ones. Is it remotely possible they have anything to do with either the quality or the quantity of your food? Look at persistent emotional and relationship problems you may have. You might think of these problems as the *cause* of overeating - but in fact they may be the *result*. (I am referring here to the effect overeating has on your self-esteem, not your weight. People with low self-esteem tend to get depressed and also to create problematic 'co-dependent' relationships).

As well as the truths you keep hidden from yourself, denial usually involves keeping things from other people as well. Most addicts keep crucial details of their addictions secret, and may even try to keep the whole addiction secret, especially from certain people. Of course, it's difficult to hide the effects of addictive eating, which is why so many overeaters become obsessed with weight loss: it's evidence that other people can see.

I'M IN CONFLICT ABOUT IT (conflict of values) – Practising an addiction means you make one value - satisfying the addiction - more important than another value - having the best possible health.

When you make your self-esteem your purpose behind taking control of your overeating, you create a new priority in your values: *I* matter here, the quality of *my* life matters, *my* health matters - to *me*. This doesn't happen automatically, and it may not feel natural at first. You need to make deliberate choices to change things, and at first you may be in conflict about it, as if you are torn in two directions.

The process of breaking free from any addiction is the process of resolving this conflict by choosing to change your priorities. This is crucial, because an addiction is strengthened by ambivalence and confusion.

IT'S SOMETHING I DO (action) – For me, one of the most fascinating aspects of addictions is that they involve behaviour - actions that really happen. However hard you may try, you can't get away from the fact of the actions you have or have not taken. You could affirm your commitment to your health over and over again, but if you then follow that up with the act of addictive eating, your self-esteem will suffer.

This can be a hard lesson to learn, but it has its bright side. Changing your actions - your behaviour - if done correctly, has tremendous psychological and spiritual rewards. As a friend of mine likes to say: often it's better to act your way into right-thinking than to think your way into right-acting.

MORE THAN YOU NEED

So an addiction is a problem, which is why, sooner or later, we want to stop doing it. But it's something we are very familiar with, which seems to comfort us and bring us pleasure, so we are 'in two minds' about what to do. Addiction involves certain actions, but these actions are supported by ways of thinking which are just as much a part of the addiction.

What distinguishes overeating from almost all other addictions is its ability to be comparatively invisible. This is because it gets so easily confused with the eating we do which is not addictive because it's completely necessary. Someone trying to stop smoking, for example, can at least clearly identify what it is they are trying to stop doing. Anyone addicted to food knows it's as addictive as any drug, but can't see exactly where their addiction begins and ends.

Some people have attempted to define food addiction by classifying certain kinds of food as addictive, such as sugar and white flour. They then advocate abstention from these, using this criterion as a way of defining addiction.

If you want to abstain completely from specific foods (perhaps you already do) because of addiction, religion, health problems such as diabetes, or any other reason, you can use everything in this book to support you in that goal. However, I'm not going to advocate complete abstinence from any foods as an inevitable solution for everybody.

I heard you breathe a sigh of relief here, but we still don't have a definition of addictive eating. Our first images, perhaps, are the most dramatic and obvious. It's a midnight binge... spoonfuls of creamy, sugary goo consumed in a semi-conscious daze... it's eating when you are depressed or angry... it's eating between meals or eating too quickly... it's eating chocolate or going back for second helpings.

Remember, though, that one characteristic common to all addictions is that they are not essential for normal living. Non-addictive eating, pleasurable as it is and should be, is the food we eat in order to stay alive and in good health.

I would like to propose a different, perhaps radical, definition of food addiction. *Food addiction is eating anything other than what it is your body needs to stay in good health.* You might eat more food than your body needs at meals, in snacks between meals or both. It's addictive if it's more than you need. Extra weight is a good clue which tells you that's what you've been doing, but it's not inevitable; it's possible to stay slim eating very addictive foods you don't need at all.

Food addiction has two aspects to it. One is in quantity: it's more food than you need, whether it's healthy food or not. The other is in quality: it's eating things you don't need at all because of their poor nutritional content (and even *anti-nutritional* content - things you would be much better off without).

So what is it that we need to eat in order to stay in the best possible health? We'll look at that in more detail later on, but let me give you a rough idea of what I'm talking about: between 1,500 and 2,000 calories a day, depending on your level of physical activity and age, with those calories obtained from food that is as close to its natural state as possible. (5)

Now the good news! *I am not going to suggest that you completely eliminate your addictive eating.* I do know, however, that you can control it - and before you can control it you need to know what it is. Our goal is first to know when we may be about to eat addictively, and then to develop the ability to do it less and less often.

In order to do that we need to take a closer look at the way an addiction works, which we'll do in the next four chapters.

WHAT PEOPLE SAY ABOUT *EATING LESS*

"I daren't think how many hours of my life I must have wasted obsessing about food, calorie counting, resisting chocolate, eating something I don't really want to 'cheer myself up', feeling guilty, weighing myself, eating something else I don't really want 'because I'm bored', hunting for clothes that don't make me look fat, complaining to my friends that it's just not fair.

Now I'm free to get on with my real life of friends and work and interests and family without the fuzz of food addiction clouding everything. I have, incidentally, lost weight and dropped a dress size."

SARAH

Taking Control

1. Next time you want to eat something, and you are fairly sure this isn't a natural hunger, wait a while, it doesn't matter how long, before going ahead and eating. What you experience is your addictive desire to eat. Observe what it is, and what it feels like to you, even if it's just for a few moments. Notice your own experience - rather than trying to fit it into a picture you may have about what an addictive desire to eat should be.

2. Start to take note (mental and/or written) of your addictive desire and your justifications for overeating.
   You may find this difficult to do at first, partly because you may judge yourself for these things and partly because the addiction wants to keep all this hidden. An addiction is always supported by lies, and when you expose a lie it's difficult to maintain. That's the point. The more you push yourself to do it, the easier it will become. Try not to judge yourself too harshly. Most people are addicted to something - caffeine, for example. Instead of condemning yourself, you could congratulate yourself for starting to do something about it.

3. As you read on, it's likely you'll have some concerns about what all this will lead to in the future. What will your life be like if you get involved with this technique? Will you be able to cope with parties, family gatherings and holidays? And will you continue to use these techniques even though you've given up on things you've tried before? You may even find that the thought of success (whatever that means to you) is just as frightening as predicting failure.
   Be careful, because although worries such as these are perfectly normal and understandable, they can easily turn into the self-fulfilling prophesy: 'I'll never be able to keep this up, so why bother trying in the first place?'
   Counteract this thinking by simply bringing yourself back to the here and now. Remind yourself that the future hasn't happened yet: it only exists in your fantasies about it. The more you stay focused on the present time - whatever is happening *right now* - the easier it will be for you to stay positive and motivated about any changes you may want to make.
   You don't have to believe this will work for you in order for it to work. You are unlikely to know anyway, until you've tried it. Be willing to not know what will happen, and see what unfolds.

6 YOUR WILL IS THE WAY

In Chapter Four we looked at the six principles which enable you to take control of your addictive eating and as a result build genuine self-esteem. Each of these principles has significance, but one in particular needs special attention with regard to addictions: self-responsibility. Avoiding responsibility is very common and something an addiction thrives on. When you begin to take more responsibility, everything else will fall in place behind that.

In this chapter we'll look at how you can do that; something which is often not at all obvious when it comes to taking control of an addiction. First of all, let's look at a situation in which you wouldn't be eating addictively, but you wouldn't be responsible for that.

Imagine for a moment what it would be like if somebody else had control of your food, so they decide when, what and how much you eat. They give you just enough food to stay alive and healthy and no more, and you don't have access to any other food. Of course this could only be accomplished if they had restrained you in some way, if you were locked up in a cell from which there was no escape. Otherwise you'd be free to run off and eat whatever you wanted.

How do you think you'd react in that situation? My guess is you would have a mixture of two completely different reactions. One would be along the lines of compliance, and the other would be some kind of rebellion.

Compliance means you go along with the way things are, even feeling grateful for being locked up because finally you are not overeating. You feel relieved and try your best to conform and to 'be good'.

Rebellion could take many different forms. You might be rude and uncooperative towards your jailers. If they wanted you to keep your cell tidy, you might rebel by messing it up. You might start to dig a secret tunnel or look for some other way to get out, by becoming ill, for example.

Your rebellion would be fuelled by your anger and resentment over the injustice of not being free to eat whatever you wanted. And when you were finally let out, you'd most likely want to devour all the things you hadn't been allowed to eat before. This is what you might call 'being bad'.

Different personalities will identify with one of these reactions more than the other, but the chances are you would experience them both in varying degrees as time went on. On one day in your cell you may think: 'oh this is great, just look at all the weight I'm losing'. But on another day all you can think about is your favourite 'comfort foods' and how much you want them and miss them - especially if you could see and smell them!

This scenario explains how you are affected by the degree to which you take responsibility for your eating. If you are locked up in the cell as I just described, you are not responsible for the quantity or the quality of the food you eat. Your jailer is.

The point is that whenever people try to eat less, they invariably mimic this situation in their minds. They create a mental attitude that imitates being locked up in a cell with only enough food to survive. This is because they don't take responsibility.

It is this that creates the cycle of alternately dieting and bingeing that so many people find themselves caught up in. They lock themselves into a diet, comply with the rules for as long as they can, then make up for lost time as soon as they've been 'released' - when they've reached a target weight, for example.

Whether you follow diets or not, the chances are you can identify with this to some degree. Any attempt to cut back on addictive eating is usually carried out through a denial of choice *- and a denial of choice is a denial of responsibility*. Maybe you say to yourself: 'I *can't* have that' or 'that's *forbidden*'. It may be: 'I'm *not allowed* to eat anything with sugar in' or 'I *mustn't* eat between meals' or 'I've *got to* stop eating so much'.

Most people fear that if they have the freedom to overeat, they will. So in order to take control they must deny that freedom to themselves.

With thoughts like these, there's only one way to go: comply for as long as you can, and then rebel. Compliance may look like control, but after living for some time with this kind of prohibitive thinking, it will feel like deprivation. Eventually, even the *thought* of compliance feels like deprivation, which is why many people will overeat the day *before* starting a diet.

This is a very big part of what addictive eating is all about. It's eating more food than you need so that you don't feel deprived.

The thing is, how much you feel deprived has very little to do with how much you are or are not eating. I'm not talking about physical deprivation in the sense of famine or starvation. The feelings of deprivation I'm talking about come from a state of mind, and that state of mind is one of resentment, created by believing you are prohibited from eating something, that you are being given rules and restrictions. It's created from thinking things like: 'I have to', 'I must', 'I'm not allowed' 'I can't' and 'I never will again'.

Here's one example of how this works that happened to me recently. As part of my research for this book I read some leaflets - the kind available at the doctors' - to see what was the official advice on nutrition these days. One of these leaflets was about keeping your heart in good shape, and it gave a list of foods that contribute to heart disease. On this list was 'pork pies'. I read it and then forgot all about it. I'm not a big pork pie eater; I may go through one or two a year. But a few days later in the supermarket I found myself drawn to a shelf full of - you guessed it - pork pies! I really wanted one, but I was also curious about this sudden interest in something I don't usually buy. Then I remembered the leaflet. Without realising, I had recorded pork pies as 'forbidden' and the rebel in me showed up as predictably as day follows night.

If I had then reacted by telling myself: 'don't you dare eat one of those!' I believe I would have made things worse, because then I would have felt deprived and wanted one even more. Instead, I gave myself permission to eat all the pork pies I want - *remembering what the consequences of doing so would be.* I gave myself a choice, and in doing so I took responsibility.

The position I take is: 'This is my body and it's up to me what goes in it. I'm in charge here. Health experts give me helpful information, but I choose whether or not I follow their advice.'

If I don't take that step, all I can do is rebel - or comply for a while and then rebel all the more.

The more I take responsibility by recognising my freedom to choose, the less I feel deprived and the less I need to rebel.

DEPRIVATION OR CHOICE

If you try to eat less by telling yourself:

I can't...   I mustn't...   I shouldn't...   I won't...
I have to stop...   I've got to stop...   I'm not allowed...
I'm not able to...   it's forbidden...   I never will again...

*You'll react as if
you were locked up
and forced to eat less:*

Either you comply:

be good and follow the rules
eat less food
feel happy and grateful
don't eat junk food
lose weight
feel relieved and successful

Or you get rebellious:

feel deprived, angry, resentful
feel miserable and martyred
can't stop thinking about food
feel guilty about eating
eat compulsively whenever a good
excuse comes along

Compliance looks good - but will lead to rebellion sooner or later!!

The solution is to tell yourself:

THIS IS MY CHOICE
I CAN EAT ANYTHING I WANT
I CAN EAT AS MUCH AS I WANT

◊ Say these things to yourself whenever you think about eating something, while you are eating and when you've finished - *especially* if it's addictive eating.

◊ Fear of failure makes free choice difficult to grasp. The fear is: "If I really can eat anything I want, I know I will!!!" Then, what follows is a denial of free choice in an attempt to eat less.

◊ You've always got free choices, no matter what the consequences of those choices may be. A bad choice is still a choice. With each choice, either to eat or not to eat something, you choose:
Either to enhance your health
Or to undermine your health

◊ When you know you've got choices, then - *and only then* - you are taking responsibility. Take responsibility and you take control!

When it comes to taking control of addictions, it makes all the difference when people genuinely take responsibility for the choices they are making. Any addictive behaviour is by its very nature irresponsible, so breaking free from addiction is inevitably a process of taking more and more responsibility.

After all, you can't be in control of something if you're not responsible for it. *This is the key: take responsibility and, as a result, you take control.*

Here are signs to watch for that will indicate to you that you are not taking as much responsibility as you could, and so will not get the long term results you want:

YOUR LANGUAGE – Become aware of the kind of language you use, both in your private thoughts and when you speak to others. What sort of things do you say to yourself? Do you use prohibitive language? Diets inevitably include a list of 'forbidden' or 'banned' foods, and diet books tell you what you are 'allowed' to eat, what you 'can't' eat and what you 'must not' or 'have to' do. If you aren't aware of this language and the powerful effect it has, it's easy to assimilate it into your own thinking. When this happens it's as if you are being made to follow orders, as if someone else is in control of you - and your addicted mind will react to that.

Another kind of command you may give yourself is: 'I'll never eat chocolate again'. Although you may be genuinely choosing this at the time, once chosen, the long-term commitment denies any choice for you in the future.

Making threats to yourself - 'you'd better not eat that' or 'don't you dare' - will have the same effect. This language imitates your jailer, who gives you commands, with threats if they aren't obeyed. So you end up feeling like you have no choice but to obey. Even if you know it's you who's doing the commanding, you'll still react as if you are being told what to do.

There are other ways of avoiding responsibility through the language you use, such as the expression: 'I found myself...' as in 'I found myself in the kitchen eating the rest of the cake'. No you didn't! First of all, you thought about the unfinished cake, then you made choices to walk into your kitchen, get the cake out of the cupboard, put it on a plate, take the plate and sit down at the table and eat the rest of the cake. You made choice after choice after choice. In a similar way, 'I fell off my diet' deviously avoids responsibility for choices you've made.

FEELING DEPRIVED – If you believe you have no choice but to eat less, sooner or later you will feel deprived, which is a feeling of self-pity and resentment. It can lead to apathy and depression and it can also create symptoms of stress. (1)

If you're more of a rebel you'll feel anger, irritability and an exaggerated addictive desire to eat: intense cravings and obsession with food.

However, if you are particularly good at being compliant you can feel entirely positive and successful for a while. Eventually, though, compliance wears thin, rebellion returns, and you are overeating again. (2)

Whenever you feel deprived of food you can be sure you have some form of prohibitive thinking going on: rules, restrictions and threats. When you change the way you are thinking, when you take responsibility by reminding yourself of your own choices, these feelings will subside.

Here's an example. For our first few sessions a recent client of mine experienced an intense addictive hunger every time she came to see me. When we talked about it, she realised that she had expected me to somehow make her or tell her to stop overeating. The stirrings of rebellion against this were automatic. After we had established that as far as I was concerned she was free to eat as much as she wanted to, the rebellious hunger disappeared.

TREATS AND REWARDS – Everybody knows forbidden fruits are the sweetest - but usually it's not fruit that gets forbidden, it's fat, salt and refined products. If you think of any food as forbidden, whenever you don't eat it you'll feel deprived, which will seem like you're being punished. So eating it will feel like a freedom and a reward - at least while you're actually eating.

If we could somehow make celery forbidden in our minds we'd think of it as a treat because we always want all the more whatever it is we think we can't, mustn't or shouldn't have. We do this because we need to know we are free. One of the worst things that can happen to any of us as human beings is to have our freedom taken away, so it's not surprising we don't like it and instinctively rebel against it. It's this instinctive attraction to something that's forbidden that adds power to our addictive desire.

If you often have strong cravings for certain kinds of food, the chances are it's because you consider them forbidden, even 'illegal', and may have done so for a long time. It's possible you'll continue to eat these foods, even though they may not be very good for you, because these are long-term, deep-seated beliefs, and they won't go away in an instant.

What I suggest is that you tell yourself before, during and after eating such foods: 'I'm allowed to eat this' and 'I can eat as much of this as I want, any time'. Give yourself permission, over and over again, to eat anything and everything you want.

I do realise you may fear giving yourself this freedom because you think you will then go ahead and eat anything and everything you want - and you may actually do some of this to begin with because at first you may recognise choice only superficially. I do want to encourage you to continue with this, though, because you will only be able to take genuine control of your eating when you have trained yourself to think in terms of the free choices you are making.

The key is choice - but in fully acknowledging this, do keep in mind the consequences of your choices, the complete picture of what it is you are actually choosing. Some choices enhance your health, others will be detrimental to it. *Instead of thinking of food as either 'allowed' or 'forbidden', think in terms of choices you make either to enhance your health or to impair it.*

STRONG COMPULSIONS TO OVEREAT – This could result from a situation where you became particularly upset about your weight. Perhaps some clothes you tried on didn't fit, or your doctor gave you a warning, or somebody made an insensitive remark about how thin and attractive you once were. Your automatic reaction is one of: 'I *have to* lose weight!' and: 'I *have to* stop eating so much!' You might at first go into a state of compliance and cut back on your addictive eating, or go straight into rebellion. Either way, you set yourself up for some serious compulsive overeating sooner or later.

Another, extreme, example is eating food that's gone bad. It's mouldy, rotten and maybe already in the rubbish bin, but the overeater who habitually takes little responsibility will feel strongly compelled to eat it, simply because it's so very much 'not allowed'. People who take so little responsibility often become stuck in a permanent state of rebellion: 'I'm not allowed to eat *anything*, so I'm going to eat *everything*, just to prove I'm free to do so'.

Most of us do a version of this, eating things mainly because we think of them as forbidden and we want to confirm to ourselves we are free to eat them if we want to. We may not be aware that this is our motivation at the time, perhaps explaining our behaviour by telling ourselves: 'I just can't resist them'. When I've eaten like that I've often (but not always) thought to myself that I don't really enjoy what I'm eating as much as I thought I would. My desire for them was more of a desire for freedom of choice than a desire for their taste or texture.

REBELLIOUS REACTION TO DIETARY ADVICE – An example of this is my pork pie story earlier in this chapter. A friend of mine provided another example. Ellen had asked me to explain the principles contained in a book I was reading about nutrition, and I told her that an example of a meal would be about 6oz of lean protein with green vegetables. My friend's instant reaction was: 'Well, that just makes me want to eat chocolate!'

I'm not suggesting you take on advice without question, simply that you consider the sense of it for yourself - and watch out for the spontaneous rebellion that occurs whenever you think that someone else might make you eat less.

STRONG DISLIKE OF NATURAL HUNGER – At the beginning of this chapter I asked you to imagine what it would feel like if you were locked up in a cell and given only just enough food to survive. Part of an entirely appropriate reaction to that situation would be anger and resentment, which you would probably feel more strongly whenever you felt genuine, natural hunger. So, lack of responsibility brings about a negative response to hunger, because it feels as if you are not freely choosing it.

JUSTIFICATIONS – If you are very attached to all the reasons you give yourself as to why you eat addictively, it's probably because you tend to deny your freedom of choice. The justifications provide you with some sort of permission to overeat.

In order to be convincing the justification must fit the circumstance: a holiday abroad, a family gathering or an evening alone can all seem equally compelling reasons to overeat. Justifications can also be found on a daily basis in any number of physical or emotional upsets.

Perhaps you can see that if you were locked up in that cell you may well conjure up an illness in order to get released. In real life this isn't deliberately chosen. It can be quite automatic and unconscious, taking the form of a stomach upset or headache, and can seem to be a very sensible reason to eat something. Justifications are tricky because they can often look perfectly reasonable. We'll look at a wider variety of justifications, and how to see through them, in Chapters Nine and Ten.

When you do begin to take more responsibility by reminding yourself you always have free choices, you will see that you don't need to justify eating anything. You can just do it. It's your choice. Then you can begin to let go of some of the justifications.

PASSIVITY – Resigning yourself to the way things are, wishing someone would come along and solve the problem for you or looking for magic cures are all good indications you are not taking responsibility yourself.

Looking for a magic pill is not going to help you. It will only serve to discourage you once you find that the magic you are looking for doesn't exist. When you take control of your overeating it is the result of the choices you and only you can make, not as a result of some gimmick that supposedly relieves you of that responsibility.

A crucial step in taking responsibility is accepting that nobody else can or should do this for you. *Not only can nobody else do this for you, but you already possess all the magic you need to get this job done.*

WHY DON'T YOU - YES BUT – This is the name of one of the games from the book *Games People Play* by Eric Berne. Played between two people, one is trying to help while the other skillfully avoids taking responsibility. It begins with the latter describing a problem they have, for example:

A: I live on my own and I cook such huge amounts, I always eat way too much.

B: Why don't you just make smaller amounts?

A: Well, I love to make minestrone soup for example, and there are so many ingredients I always end up with a great big potful.

B: Why don't you freeze some of it, in separate containers?

A: It doesn't freeze well, it loses its flavour.

B: Why don't you keep it in the refrigerator and have it over a few days?

A: Yes, I try to do that sometimes but I find I eat it all in one evening. When it's there, it's so good I just want to keep eating it until it's finished.

B: Why don't you make minestrone only when you've got people coming over who can share it with you?

A: I just do a main course when I have company, like a pasta dish. I wouldn't want to make minestrone as well - I'd be spending all day in the kitchen!

This game is usually played out with someone else, which is one reason I advise you not to discuss with your family and friends anything you define as a 'problem' you have with eating: you're likely to end up playing the game! If it seems as if someone else is trying to take responsibility for your addictive eating, they might be welcomed initially (compliance) but ultimately resisted and resented (rebellion).

You might find yourself playing 'Why Don't You - Yes, But' with me as you read through this book. I may make a suggestion, and you automatically react with a 'yes, but' objection to it. In fact, as I reread chapters I've already written, *I* sometimes react with an 'yes, but' objection to it. Yes, I can be irresponsible too! I'd like someone to come along and take care of all my problems for me. For a long time I wanted someone to come along and write this book for me. I put off writing it for years because it seemed so difficult I wouldn't take responsibility for doing it myself. But finally, I took responsibility for writing it and you have the result of that in your hands. Taking responsibility produces results. If 'A' took responsibility, she would find her own solution.

And that's precisely where the growing up takes place; when we own our problems and recognise that we are the source of the solutions. Especially when it comes to eating, because that can be so completely within our control.

WAY OF LIFE – Avoiding taking responsibility is, of course, a way of life which extends far beyond eating issues. Especially common among overeaters are those people who take on far too much responsibility for others, behaviour which is sometimes referred to as 'relationship addiction'. They are the obsessive care-takers and rescuers whose lives revolve around trying to sort out other peoples' problems. *They take responsibility for everyone but themselves.*

Low self-esteem drives this way of life: it's another attempt to gain self-worth through pleasing or fixing things for others. People who live like this may appear to be saints and martyrs, but they drop out on their responsibilities to themselves, and so lose out on true self-esteem.

They may justify their lack of responsibility by telling themselves: 'I would look after myself more, but I'm so preoccupied with looking after him/her/them, I can't possibly cope with it all - if only they sorted their lives out, then I'd be able to sort myself out.'

If you recognise yourself in this, it will be important for you to make changes here too, in order to get into the habit of taking more responsibility for yourself. Simply refuse to rescue others by refusing to assume responsibility for them. Allow them to be who they are and to make their own mistakes. By detaching yourself in this way, you will be inviting them to take responsibility for themselves - which is really all they need to do.

I'm not suggesting you should stop caring about them. In fact, allowing others to take responsibility for themselves is the most caring thing you can do for them. What I'm suggesting is that you stop trying to make other people do what you think they should do. Stop trying to control others, and you will free yourself up to take control of yourself. (3)

By the way, if you see yourself in these words, notice if you're reading this book mostly with other people in mind. It's very likely that many things will apply to people you know, but you could be ignoring it's relevance *to you* by thinking in terms of what other people need to learn. For example, Susan, an overweight friend of mine who read the manuscript of this book, did nothing about her own eating, but started to give advice to friends and family about theirs. The advice, need I say, was not appreciated.

By all means let people know about this book if you think they may benefit from reading it, but I strongly advise you to be cautious as to how you speak about it, if at all.

WILLPOWER - AND HOW TO USE YOURS

Willpower is quite literally the power of your will, and the most important thing to understand about your will is that it is *free.* Your will is in your power to freely choose what you will and what you will not do. When you deny your freedom of choice you deny your free will - *and you can't possibly use your will effectively while you deny it.*

This is how you undermine your willpower. When someone says: 'I have no willpower' it's the same as saying: 'I'm not taking responsibility for my choices.'

The solution is in your acknowledgment of choice. The most common error is to consider the consequences of a certain choice and then to conclude that you have no choice. So watch out for lines of thinking such as:

- 'If I want to lose weight, then I *have to* stop eating so much.'
- 'If I want to stay in control of my eating, then I *can't* eat any more ice cream.'
- 'If I take responsibility for my eating, then I *won't be able to* eat everything I want.'

This is *false reasoning.* You can want something sincerely, even desperately, but this never removes your free choice in the matter. The only time you wouldn't have completely free choices about your eating decisions is if you were locked up in that cell. You wouldn't be overeating, but it wouldn't be your choice. You wouldn't be responsible. Whenever you notice this way of thinking, correct it to thoughts such as these:

- 'Yes, I do want to lose weight, but I could continue to overeat and put on even more.'
- 'I do want to stay in control of my eating, but I still have the option of eating addictively.'
- 'Taking responsibility means knowing I am able to eat anything and everything I want.'

I'm not suggesting you go ahead and eat everything you want! What I'm saying is, if you remind yourself you *can* eat anything you want, then you will be able to make a choice. You need to know you have a choice before you can make one.

You might resist acknowledging choice because you then blame yourself and feel guilty for choices you've made in the past. Perhaps you take being responsible to mean: 'It's all my fault'. But blaming yourself is not the same as taking responsibility; it's judging yourself.

Taking responsibility means independent thought and independent decision making. You take responsibility when you recognise that you are the one who determines what you do, that your actions are up to you and nobody else. You take responsibility for your health by acknowledging that your physical well-being is up to you and nobody else.

Which choices are going to support our health and which will undermine it may not always be clear, and it's inevitable we'll get it wrong sometimes. We have so much choice when it comes to food! We are confronted with decisions all through our day regarding what to eat and when to eat it, what is good for us and what is harmful, how much of it to eat, and whether or not it really is what we want at that time.

So often, though, we abdicate and either go with our own traditions or follow what everyone else is doing. So often we simply adopt the choices that others have made: our family, our peers, our culture, the food industry. Taking responsibility means gaining some knowledge of the facts, and then examining and challenging the assumptions we're making about what we're eating.

Taking responsibility is a process of growing up. When we were infants we were not responsible for what we ate. Taking more responsibility is a long process which begins when we first put food into our own mouths. Then we begin to make our own choices about what we will and will not eat, and eventually learn to shop and cook for ourselves or go out to restaurants and order our own meals.

As infants we demanded instant gratification; the ability to delay gratification is something we learn to do as we mature. Maybe you don't want to be grown-up, but what's nice is to have the ability to be either child-like or adult, as we want. (4)

Taking more responsibility isn't a decision you make once and that's it. It's not a permanent state. But when you develop the habit of recreating it over and over, it becomes easier with practice and more natural. The point is simply to begin. You will start to feel better immediately.

You'll know when you're doing it because you will be able to make changes in your eating and feel good about those changes. You'll feel more powerful and more hopeful that you've got something which will last.

You'll know when you're doing it because you won't feel deprived when you choose not to eat something. This is why taking responsibility is essential in taking control of addiction. It's very difficult to stay motivated if it feels as if you are depriving yourself.

You'll know when you're taking more responsibility because you will experience less guilt and higher self-esteem. This is why self-esteem is a more effective motivation than losing weight. You may lose weight while you are 'locked up' in a diet, but if you are not taking responsibility - owning your own choices - your self-esteem may not improve.

No matter what happens, you are going to be thinking about food, on and off, for the rest of your life. You'll have thoughts about food every day, at many times throughout the day. You don't have a choice about that! What you do have a choice about is the quality of those thoughts. If you begin to think in ways that cultivate a more responsible relationship with food, the benefit to you will become obvious.

This isn't an easy, magic solution, but genuine self-esteem is your reward, and my hope for you is that you discover just how exciting that can be.

In our next chapter we'll look at what choices you might make and how to go about putting choice into practise.

WHAT PEOPLE SAY ABOUT *EATING LESS*

" *I was anorexic for only a short time before developing a compulsive eating and bingeing problem which I now recognise as rebelling against being inside a box of prohibitions against certain food in certain amounts.*

After several successful years of psychotherapy, I resolved most of the emotional issues I linked with food and eating. But to my disappointment I still suffered from addictive behaviour, including compulsive eating, overeating, compulsive exercise and eating too little. I believed that discipline was the answer: eat enough, but not too much.

But trying harder was fruitless until I accepted freedom and responsibility. It wasn't more rules I needed. It was the knowledge that I was free to eat when and what I wanted: free to starve myself; free to exercise or not; free to binge. Only when I accepted that I was free to take any of these actions could I take responsibility for my choices.

Now, when I'm presented with a choice about food or exercise, I remind myself that I am free to do anything. Then, I ask myself what I want to do. Sometimes I get it wrong, but fine-tuning is part of living. "

SANDRA

Taking Control

1. Say to yourself: 'This is my choice' every time you eat, *especially* if you regard it as addictive or 'fattening'.

2. Say to yourself: 'I can eat anything I want' every time you think about eating something. When you are in a restaurant, let yourself know you can have anything on the menu. When you are shopping for food, tell yourself you can choose to buy anything in the shop.

   It may be true that you *can't* have everything exactly the way you want it. You *can't* keep eating everything you want and have that not affect your health and self-esteem. But even though you don't have a choice about which consequences follow from certain actions, you still have free choices about which actions you take.

3. Keep your addictive thoughts and the decisions you make about them to yourself. As much as possible, don't discuss why you are or are not eating something. If anybody makes a comment about what you are eating, just don't get involved in a conversation about it.

4. Possibly the most powerful denial of choice is created by the belief that you 'have to' lose weight (or 'can't' put on any more) and your attachment to this belief may be so strong that it alone causes your feelings of deprivation.

   You may want to lose weight, but this is quite different from not having freedom of choice in the matter. The only time you would have to lose weight (i.e. you would have no choice) is if you were locked up in a cell and given very little food. While you believe you have to lose weight, you create a state of mind as if you were locked up and so create overwhelming feelings of deprivation and then rebellion.

   If it's difficult for you to understand that you don't *have to* lose weight, try this written exercise. Write down as many endings as you can to the sentence: 'I have to lose weight because...' leaving one line blank in between each ending. This identifies the thinking behind your false belief. Then go back over what you have written and in each blank line write the true statement.

For example:

I have to lose weight because I can't get into my clothes. *(false)* I could put on even more weight and go out and buy clothes in larger sizes. *(true)*

I'm not encouraging you to put on weight, I'm encouraging you to see that you've got choices, so you won't feel deprived whenever you don't eat something. Then, as a result, you begin to move out of the compliance/rebellion cycle.

5. Some people create feelings of deprivation, not because they believe 'I have to lose weight', but because they believe 'I have to control my eating' or 'I have to eat less' or 'I have to stop overeating'. The 'I have to' and 'I can't' statements create the same problems described above, and the written exercise can be applied in the same way. Simply start your sentence with 'I have to stop overeating because...' (or words that fit best for you) and proceed in the same way.

6. Write down six endings to: 'If I take 5% more responsibility for my eating...' Write down whatever comes to your mind: there are no 'right' answers. Here are some endings from clients of mine:

    ...I won't eat the leftovers from my children's plates.
    ...I'll eat more vegetables.
    ...I'll eat less.
    ...I'll feel a lot better about myself.
    ...I'll feel more in control of my eating.
    ...I'll be a lot happier.

Notice that the first three lines refer to specific changes in behaviour and the second three are the benefits you feel from making those changes. Notice if your endings contain examples of both types. I suggest you do this exercise as often as you can; once a day would be good.

This exercise is an example of those contained in Dr. Branden's *The Six Pillars of Self Esteem*.

7   WHAT TO DO ABOUT WANTING MORE

Whenever we make a choice about anything it makes sense for us to understand what it is we are choosing. We make the best choices by knowing as much as possible about the alternatives available. When it comes to making choices about an addiction, people often think rather simplistically in terms of: shall I do it or shall I not do it? When we think like this, we overlook a crucial factor in our decision making process. This is our addictive desire.

The addictive desire is the driving force behind any addictive behaviour. Whether someone smokes a cigarette or takes cocaine or overeats, what they are doing is satisfying their particular addictive desire. For example, a smoker has an addictive desire to smoke and so they light a cigarette to satisfy it. They satisfy it and they reinforce it at the same time. It's only satisfied temporarily, of course, and before long the smoker will feel another desire, and another cigarette will be smoked. All addictions work the same way: first a desire to do whatever it is you're addicted to, and then doing it, which reinforces the addiction, creating the next addictive desire, and so on.

As someone who overeats, you have been satisfying and reinforcing your addictive desire to eat, possibly every day, for many years. The only other reason there is to eat would be a genuine need for nutrition, which is often (but not always) identified by the natural body signal of stomach hunger.

Many people never feel their natural hunger because they feed their addictive hunger before their natural hunger appears. The more extra weight a person has on them, the less they eat because of genuine hunger. More often they eat to feed their addiction.

Now we get to the biggest and most common mistake people make when they want to control an addiction: usually people try to take control of addictive behaviour by trying to avoid feeling their addictive desire. They reason that if they don't feel it, they won't feed it, and so assume they will be in control. Most smokers throw away their cigarettes and avoid temptations such as pubs and smoking friends.

In the same way, those people who know they eat addictively at home in the evenings may make plans to keep themselves extra busy - the cinema one night, tennis the next, work late another night - all in a determined effort to keep themselves from experiencing their addictive desire to eat.

This kind of strategy, in case you don't already know from experience, is flawed. It's flawed because its success depends on you not having an addictive desire, and that can only be a temporary solution.

You might, for example, decide to stop eating chocolate and not have any interest in eating chocolate for a few days. You think you're doing well because you're sticking to your intention, but I want to suggest to you that you're not accomplishing as much as you could. As you may well know, as soon as your desire resurfaces and you are lusting after your favourite chocolate treat, you eat it. This is because you never faced your addictive desire in the first place. Or, you do experience your desire for chocolate, but you see this desire as nothing but negative - something to be feared, resented and, if at all possible, eliminated.

Unless you begin to deal with your addictive desire in a more positive way, it doesn't matter how well-intentioned you are and it doesn't matter how long you have abstained. It may look for periods of time like you're in control, but all that's happening is you just aren't having a strong enough addictive desire or maybe no desire at all. Or you feel it but you're fighting it, so it's only a matter of time before you give in to it.

Whether you're making a New Year resolution not to eat chocolate, going on a diet or cutting out fried foods, the familiar scenario is to start but not to continue. You might explain this by saying it's because you don't have any willpower or that you're incapable of discipline. The real explanation is more likely to be that your addictive desire was initially avoided, and when it could no longer be avoided, it got satisfied.

How much chocolate or fried food you eat is not the point here. The real question is: are you willing, ever, under any circumstances, to deal with your addictive desire to eat? As far as taking control of an addiction goes, that's where it all takes place.

You can't take control of an addiction by avoiding it or wishing it would go away. It's only when you come to terms with your addictive desire that things will really start to change. This way may not be so easy, especially to begin with, but I promise you that the rewards are both profound and lasting.

Unlike other addictions, though, you aren't going to stop eating entirely, so your first step to dealing with your addictive desire to eat is identifying it in the first place. How can you be sure whether or not you are about to satisfy your addictive desire or your nutritional needs?

As we saw in Chapter Five, it's impossible to define addictive eating *precisely*; nobody will ever be able to say exactly where this addiction begins and ends. This doesn't mean it doesn't exist or that it can't be recognised and managed.

In fact, it's impossible to say *precisely* where a great many things begin and end - a mountain, the dawn or your ankle, to name a few examples. Nobody can say at which exact point your leg becomes your ankle and your ankle becomes your foot. This doesn't mean you don't have an ankle, that you can't use it or point to it and say: that's my ankle!

In the same way, we can point to addictive eating and say in general terms that it's eating anything other than what it is your body needs to stay in good health. The problem with addiction, though, is that it's out to deceive you, because that's what an addiction does. Your addictive thinking will have you convinced your leg goes all the way to your toes if that will justify eating another slice of cake!

What we need to do is find some way to know for sure. We need some kind of structure with boundaries that will be tougher to dispute.

The solution is contained in two very simple tools. These tools are called Times and Plans. First of all, I'll explain what I mean by these terms, then we'll take a look at how to use them to get control of your addictive eating.

TIMES

The purpose of the 'Time' is to give you a way to choose to start eating which is least likely to be influenced by your addictive thinking.

This is how you use this tool. Whenever you finish eating, whether it's a meal or a snack, set a time for yourself, and your goal is to get to that Time without eating anything. My suggestion, at least to begin with, is that you set a Time at least one hour on and no more than four hours on. For example, you finish your lunch at 1.30pm and you set a Time of 4.30pm. What you have done is to set yourself a goal of not eating anything at all until 4.30pm.

Then, when 4.30 comes, you don't have to eat at your Time. You have a choice, either to eat something and when you've finished set another Time, or to set another Time without having eaten anything.

By setting Times you will be able to gain a real sense of control over your eating. It may be difficult to know whether or not you are about to eat more than your body really needs, but you can be absolutely sure of whether or not it's 4.30!

PLANS

The purpose of the 'Plan' is to give you a way to choose when to *stop* eating which is least likely to be influenced by your addictive thinking.

This is how you use this tool. The idea is to decide what you intend to eat at that meal, just before you start eating, before you take the first bite. You decide how many portions, what size portions, how many courses, how many second helpings you plan to eat at that meal.

You don't need to weigh food or measure it too exactly, and you don't need to have it all in front of you to start with. The idea is to create, just before you begin to eat, a mental picture of what it's all going to be, as accurate as you can judge. (You might begin to plan days earlier when shopping for the week; the idea is to finalise the Plan at the point when you start the meal).

Of course you always have complete control over choosing what your Times and Plans will be. It makes sense to set a Time when you think you'll be ready to eat again, but you'll need to learn through trial and error how far apart to set the Times and how much you really do need to Plan at each meal. Undereating can be just as much of a problem as overeating. As you go along with this and gain more control over your eating, you will learn what to Plan at each meal so you'll be ready for more food when your next meal is due.

After you've gained some experience with this, and on the days when it fits your schedule and your nutritional needs, you can make the Times further apart and/or make the Plans smaller - but *this isn't the main purpose of using these tools.* The real value is that by using Times and Plans you will be able to see your addiction more clearly - and it's only when you see your addiction that you can get to work on taking control of it.

You see, sooner or later you'll want to eat something before you get to your Time. And it's inevitable you'll want to eat something more when you get to the end of a meal that wasn't included in your Plan. This is your addictive desire to eat, and - believe it or not - this desire is your golden opportunity to make real and lasting changes in your relationship with food.

The point at which you take control of an addiction is when you are experiencing your addictive desire. At the time you are wanting to eat addictively. In that experience you have a chance to open a door and walk through, and when you do you'll find yourself on the other side of something.

You'll be stepping out of your 'comfort zone', but you'll gain the ability to be in control of your addiction. Real control.

I do realise, though, that this could be sounding unrealistic to you at first. I know I'm suggesting something quite unusual, and it's understandable if you're doubtful and hesitant at first. All you need to do is keep an open mind. First of all, let's take a look at this desire and see what we can do about it.

GAINING ACCEPTANCE OF YOUR ADDICTIVE DESIRE TO EAT

UNDERSTAND IT – Your addictive desire is a thought which pops into your mind and says: *let's eat!* When it's strong enough there's usually a sense of urgency to it, as if it has to be acted on immediately.

It comes into your mind as you get reminded by many different things - places, people, thoughts, moods, stress, times of day, routines, physical ailments - which you have conditioned yourself to associate with eating in the past.

Often a particular cue will trigger a desire to eat a particular thing. For example, you go somewhere and remember you ate crisps when you where there last time, and so you want crisps again, even though you may rarely think of them in other circumstances.

Most people can identify addictive patterns in their eating: what they tend to eat whenever they're alone at home, whenever they're upset, whenever it's four o'clock, whenever they go to the cinema.

This eating has little or nothing to do with nutrition and everything to do with the conditioned response which is at the heart of all addictive behaviour.

IDENTIFY IT – Sometimes the addictive desire can be so subtle you don't even notice it. It can be a very simple, reasonable, everyday sort of thought, flickering through your mind, which suggests you eat something. If some food is on its way into your mouth, it's quite possible you are experiencing, and are about to satisfy and reinforce, your addictive desire to eat. Becoming aware of that is the first step to taking control.

At other times, though, your addictive desire will feel stronger, like a void that wants to be filled. It will feel quite uncomfortable if it's not satisfied. It may well feel like hunger, and it may be difficult for you to know whether it's an addictive desire or a genuine need for food.

So how can you be sure it is addictive? Well, if it's before your Time or after your Plan, then you know it's addictive. And if it's a desire for crisps it's addictive because you don't need them in order to stay in good health.

CHOOSE IT – Just because you have an addictive desire to eat this doesn't mean you have to satisfy it. You have a choice. You'll know from our last chapter that if you forget you're making choices, your addictive desire will become exaggerated. It can become exaggerated in different ways:

- it can become more frequent, so you want to eat more often
- it can become more intense, turning into a strong craving
- it can become longer in duration, as a persistent nagging.

For example, you might experience an intense addictive desire as soon as you set a Time because you assume you then *can't* eat anything until you get to that Time. You may even resist setting Times in the first place because it feels like you're putting yourself into the no-choice cell of deprivation.

It's going to be draining to try to control your eating in a context of deprivation, so remember, every time you feel an addictive desire to eat, you always have a choice as to whether or not you satisfy it. *Remind yourself that you don't have to do any of this, and you will be able to regard Times and Plans as tools to use rather than rules to obey.*

If you still don't fully understand this distinction reread Chapter Six, working on the exercises at the end. If this information about choice is new to you, it may take a while for it to become real to you. This doesn't mean it won't work for you eventually, it just means you need to be persistent. Keep reminding yourself that you can eat anything, any time, as much as you want. Then, make the genuine choices you really do want to live with.

FEEL IT – Although the desire may be experienced physically as a sensation in your body, it's helpful to remember it's coming from your mind. This is something that happens with all addictive desires. For example, research on addiction has demonstrated that abstaining cocaine addicts will experience their addictive desire as a physical feeling, and that this can be brought on simply by watching a video of people taking cocaine. (1)

In the same way, you may have a desire to eat simply because you see or smell food or because you see other people eating. With food, though, you don't need to watch someone else doing it because you will be doing it yourself when it comes to dinner time! The process of eating a meal will often trigger the addictive desire in you. I wouldn't be surprised if you have experienced this many times in the past. You begin a meal not so very interested in eating, but by the end of the meal your addictive desire is in full swing and you want to go on and on and on and on.

SEEK IT OUT – I hope you can see that if you could get to a point where you simply let yourself experience those feelings of desire instead of feeding them, and without getting upset about them, then you'd be in a very powerful position of control. You'd be able to say: 'yes, that second helping looks wonderful and I know I would enjoy eating it, but I'm choosing to accept this feeling of desire instead of satisfying it.' And you'd be able to do that any time, with any food you desired.

I'm not suggesting you make this change in an instant. I'm simply suggesting you consider going in that direction. Take it at your own speed - which you will, anyway! However, if you want to speed the process up, you can work on inducing your desire. What this means is you deliberately seek it out and conjure it up.

Availability makes any addictive desire stronger, so you could buy something you love, and keep it around you for a while. Consider any thought you have about it to be your addictive desire to eat, along with justifications for satisfying that desire. Another thing you can do is to leave food on your plate at the end of a meal, making sure it's a bite or two of your favourite morsel. The point is to finish your meal wanting more. Bring that addictive desire out and choose to let yourself feel it. This is the most powerful technique to use because this way you directly confront the addiction.

FACE IT DIRECTLY – A diet/weight loss way of thinking will lead you to substitute something 'innocent' in an attempt to satisfy your addictive desire, and as a result you can end up consuming enormous quantities of things such as sunflower seeds, lettuce, tea or water. For the same reason, a pot of low-fat yoghourt gets substituted for a high-fat, high-sugar dessert at the end of a meal.

I met a weight-loss group leader once who told me she would eat four heads of iceberg lettuce at once, with no dressing. Clearly she was feeding an addictive desire for something else, and clearly her motivation was not to gain weight.

When your motivation is to take control of your overeating, you choose between feeding your addictive desire or to accept feeling it. Trying to find a 'cottage cheese compromise' will do nothing but hinder your progress.

BE AWARE OF IT – Repression is an automatic coping mechanism we all have the power to employ. Automatic means it's not consciously chosen. For example, many people automatically repress their feelings of anger. They were probably taught as children that the expression of anger was unacceptable, and so they learned to feel it as little as possible in order to stay 'in control'.

In the same way, your addictive desire to eat can become repressed for periods of time simply because you regard it as unacceptable. It's very likely you've learned to repress your addictive desire while you go on diets.

There's another way the addictive desire can disappear for a while. Whenever people over-indulge their addiction, whether it's food, alcohol, cocaine or whatever, the binge is inevitably followed by an initial 'crash' phase with no addictive desire at all. Aversive thoughts will predominate - guilt, together with nausea and physical discomfort - which override any desire for more food. The desire returns in time, of course, when the crash phase has passed.

Many overeaters go through 'binge/fast' cycles in this way. The 'fast' phase of the cycle may seem to be your ideal state - but it doesn't mean you're in control of your addiction while you have no addictive desire. *It's the presence of the desire, not its absence, that gives you the opportunity to take control.*

VALUE IT – Providing you really do believe you are freely choosing to accept your desire, it's possible for you to see it as a positive experience. It will be helpful for you to focus on what you are gaining in self-control and self-esteem, not on what you are losing - a second slice of cake, for example. See it as a trade-off: 'I could eat the cake, but if I accept this desire I have for the cake I stay in control of my eating.' (I'm assuming the second slice of cake wasn't part of your Plan).

By building a positive response to your addictive desire, you gradually diminish the power of your addiction to food. In fact, the strength of your addiction could be measured in terms of how much you don't want to feel your addictive desire to eat.

This is what leads you to be out of control in the first place. When you are not prepared to accept your feelings of desire, you are at the mercy of your addiction and its whims. You eat whenever you happen to have a desire to do so, and sometimes this may mean you'll be eating all day long.

A binge is an unsuccessful attempt to satisfy an addictive desire. Your attempts to satisfy it keep it going, especially when it's fuelled by a persistent emotion such as anger or loneliness. As it's impossible to satisfy, the desire only abates when you become preoccupied with thoughts of self-loathing.

So one reason to accept and value the uncomfortable feeling of desire is because not accepting it is more uncomfortable in its own way. *Then you can stop trying to satisfy something that is fundamentally unsatisfiable.*

THE ADDICTIVE DESIRE TO EAT

The scientist Pavlov found that dogs could be trained to expect food (they salivated) whenever a light flashed, simply because the light flashed when they had been fed in the past. Here is a list of things which may trigger your desire to eat, by association, simply because you ate in response to these things in the past.

Consider how many times you have reinforced this connection. This is not to try to make you feel guilty; it's so you can accept the fact that this connection isn't going to magically disappear. It fades in time when you no longer reinforce it, provided you are genuinely choosing to feel it.

Places - shops, restaurants, your kitchen, your car, the cinema, the pub, your work place

Circumstances - cooking, family gatherings, being offered food, being with someone else who is eating, travelling

Time of day - mid-morning, 1 o'clock (= lunch time), mid-afternoon, time to go to bed

Your senses - sight, smell and taste of food (perhaps while shopping for food, cooking and/or eating)

'Negative' emotions - boredom, sadness, frustration, anger, self-pity, fear, anxiety, embarrassment, regret, loneliness, rejection

'Positive' emotions - celebration, relaxation, accomplishment, feelings of connection and intimacy

Physical sensations - aches and pains, changes in menstrual cycle, symptoms of stress, feeling tired, drop in blood sugar

Altered states of consciousness - being drunk or under the influence of 'recreational' drugs

- Some of these associations may be made unconsciously. In other words, you aren't consciously aware of the cue and/or you aren't aware of your addictive desire to eat. You 'just find yourself wanting to eat' or you 'just find yourself eating'. Times and Plans will help you gain awareness of your addictive desire to eat. It's not essential to identify every cue.

- You could experience two or more of these cues simultaneously, and possibly natural hunger as well. Use the tools of Times and Plans to determine when and how much to eat.

- Remember, it's your choice: either satisfy and reinforce your addictive desire or accept it as an uncomfortable feeling which brings you some kind of improvement in the quality of your life.

RESOLVE THE CONFLICT IT PRESENTS – A state of conflict arises when you want two different things at once and you can't have both of them:

1. you want to stay in control of your addictive eating *and*
2. you experience your addictive desire to eat.

This is the essence of withdrawal from addiction - a conflict which may initially feel like a battle.

I want to suggest to you that it's your wanting to avoid this conflict that has contributed to your long term failure to take control of your eating in the past. You see, you need to go through the conflict in order to take genuine control. It's the inevitable difficulty involved in making real change.

The battle will diminish in time. Addictive eating reinforces addictive eating, because whenever you feed an addictive desire you strengthen it. When you choose to accept the desire you diminish it. So, the way to weaken your addiction is to become willing to accept feeling your addictive desire. Then you resolve the conflict, not by avoiding the desire but by surrendering to it.

SURRENDER TO IT – The less you fight and resent feeling your addictive desire, the more quickly you resolve the conflict it presents. Simply allow yourself to feel it, because it's your resistance to it that makes it more persistent.

There are people who deal with their emotions in the same way. Many people, perhaps as a result of personal development training or therapy of various kinds, believe in the principle of letting themselves feel their feelings. They think positively about having 'negative' feelings, whatever they are. They accept that these difficult emotions are part of life and that to face them is more beneficial to them than trying to avoid and ignore them. What I'm suggesting here is that, for similar reasons, another sort of feeling that is very beneficial to face is your addictive desire to eat. (2)

DO IT YOURSELF – Being in a state of desire and conflict is difficult and uncomfortable. If you attempt to do that in order to gain approval from others you are likely to feel martyred, and this is likely to backfire on you in some way. Remember from Chapter Three that wanting to lose weight is a motivation that is *primarily* about what others think of you.

You will run into big problems if you try to resolve this conflict in order to please or impress others by 'looking good'. It's your very private experience of higher genuine self-esteem and improved health and vitality that leaves you feeling like you've gained something when you choose to accept feeling your addictive desire, instead of feeling like you're missing out on something.

LAUGH AT IT – Whenever you feel an addictive desire to eat, either before your Time or after your Plan, your first reaction may be to blame yourself, perhaps judging yourself as greedy, indulgent or worse. Accepting your desire also means accepting yourself for having the desire, realising that the only reason you're feeling it is because you ate addictively in the past.

Forgiving yourself for the overeating you've done in the past is essential, and a sense of humour about it and about yourself will help you a great deal.

APPLYING TIMES AND PLANS

I hope you don't underestimate the value of Times and Plans. The technique may at first seem too simple, but its effectiveness lies in its simplicity. It's flexible from day to day, adaptable to your unique needs and, most importantly, self-determined. It's a very powerful technique - but only if you use and value it. It will work very well for you if you use it in a rigorous way. If you use it halfheartedly you will get halfhearted results.

Here are some of the finer details about putting this technique into practice:

- *Drinking:* There's no need to set Times and make Plans for drinking liquids. Be aware, though, if you are trying to satisfy your addictive desire to eat by drinking.
- *Watching the clock:* If you find yourself frequently checking to see if it's your Time yet, know that this is your addictive desire. You'll find it works a lot better to make a deliberate choice to accept the desire, reminding yourself why you are doing that, rather than impatiently waiting for your Time.

- *Forgetting to set a Time or setting one and then forgetting what it is:* Set yourself a Time as soon as you realise you don't have one. Just make sure it's at least one hour after you last ate, and it would be best if it's a somewhat challenging space of time ahead. Some people write their Times down if they keep forgetting them.
- *Going past the Time without realising:* Either eat or set a new Time.
- *You don't know when your food will arrive, so you aren't sure when to set the Time:* For example, you know you'll want to eat when you get home, but you don't know exactly when you're getting home. Or you're at a restaurant or someone else's house for a meal.

  It's fine, for example, to set a Time of, say, 6pm or 'whenever I get home', so long as you then don't start to rearrange your schedule to arrive home earlier! The same applies to food that's being prepared for you by someone else.
- *Setting the same Times every day:* It's OK to have some standard Times, for example, to always eat lunch at 1pm. For many people various commitments will make this necessary. However it's always better to consider your nutritional needs as much as possible, instead of keeping in a routine just because it is a routine.
- *Eating while cooking:* When cooking for yourself you could include the cooking in your Time and Plan, and eat some while preparing it. It's after your Time and included in your Plan, so there's no problem. Otherwise, be very aware of whether you're tasting something to see if it's cooked and seasoned properly or whether you're swallowing mouthfuls in an addictive way.

  One of the liberating things about this technique is that you don't have to worry about whether you're eating too fast, or eating while you're standing up, travelling, talking, reading or watching TV.
- *Starting a meal while you feel strong addictive hunger:* Your addictive desire could continue for some time, especially if it's tied up with a persistent mood, and this is another value in using Times and Plans. There will be some days when you feel an addictive desire to eat on and off all day, but if you stick to Times and Plans - because you do need to eat sometimes - you'll know you're in control.

- *Setting Times and Plans, sticking to them, but still feeling like you've eaten too much:* Estimating exactly how much you need to eat will always be guesswork. You can do this in a controlled way, though, by using the techniques. Just remember for next time. It's perfectly normal to eat more on some days, and less on others.
- *Eating from a buffet or shared bowl:* Make your Plan by selecting what and how much you are going to eat and putting it on your own plate or napkin. If you want to include a second helping in your Plan, be clear about what that's going to be before you take the first bite.
- *Planning something that later turns out to be unavailable, a dessert in a restaurant for example:* This is a valid reason to change your Plan. Another is a genuine health need, such as a hypoglycemic attack. Otherwise, to eat unplanned is to eat addictively.

I NEVER DENY MYSELF!

A client of mine said this to me recently with a look in her eyes that said: 'and don't you dare suggest that I should do so!' She was telling me that if she has a strong desire to eat something, she has every intention of going ahead and satisfying that desire, and she has every right to do so. Of course she does have every right to do so, and I'm not going to tell her what choices to make. But she will have to live with the consequences which come from consistently following that course of action - consequences she was not happy with, which was why she was seeing me in the first place.

At first glance, accepting a strong addictive desire to eat may sound like a fate worse than death - but take a look at the possibilities here. A lot of things fall into place when, instead of thinking it shouldn't be there or trying to make it go away, you come to an acceptance of your addictive desire. In order to achieve this, you will need to struggle through some real conflict, otherwise you will just be skimming over the surface of the problem.

The biggest mistake people make is they try to find an easy solution which eliminates their desire. Taking control of addictive behaviour is always difficult. It's not impossible, but it requires some effort. What makes it more possible is realising that it does require effort. Trying to avoid that truth makes it worse, because then as soon as it gets difficult you are incapable of dealing with it. You set yourself up for failure simply because you are not willing to face that difficulty.

You can continue to resist and resent the difficulty of controlling your eating. Or you can see that this is an inevitable part of the process and regard the difficulty as the sign you are beginning to take control.

There may be days when you feel your addictive hunger on and off all day long. The more you have, the better, because that's when you practice dealing with your problem. *The decisions that are the toughest to make are where you will make the most progress.*

All this will take time, so be patient with yourself. All you need to do is keep at it, and there will come a time when you become much more willing to accept your addictive desire to eat. Regard every obstacle as an opportunity. For most overeaters this is a very old problem, and it takes a lot of careful thought to turn around, but in time, as you continue to use these techniques, your addictive desire will become less and less of a problem for you.

Experience your compulsion to overeat and make your peace with it. It's the sign you are not overeating. It's the sign you are keeping your word to yourself. It's the way you apply the brakes. It means you no longer need to be afraid of situations which you associate with addictive eating. It means you can create, in the words of another client of mine, a relationship with food that is 'a source of contentment and even euphoria, rather than an abiding sorrow.'

After all these words about desire, I do want to make the point that at times in the past you must have made choices to accept feeling your addictive desire to eat, even though you could have satisfied it. My purpose in this chapter is to encourage you to do that more deliberately, more powerfully and more consistently.

For some people, though, there can be physical conditions that makes this process more difficult. This is what we'll look at next.

WHAT PEOPLE SAY ABOUT *EATING LESS*

"When I used to diet, I was often able to push the thought of food away. But I knew it would always come back, and it always did. And I was unprepared. Now, when the desire to eat more than I need comes up (and it still comes up!) I take it as an opportunity to discover what it really is that I want.

Now, the desire to eat is no longer the monster that was always lurking in the background. I am able to recognise it, take a look, and try to establish contact. It's still there, but I know it so much better, much better than I ever thought I would. Sometimes we are fighting each other, but I don't feel helpless any more.

When faced with a chocolate cake, I would desire it intensely. It was almost like being in love. At the same time, I knew I shouldn't eat it. So I ate it and felt bad. Now, I still sometimes eat it, though most often I don't. But now it is no longer the one I love. It's just a chocolate cake.

The way to get through your addiction is not by denying it or trying to avoid it (which you can't anyway) but by experiencing it. This is a very important and exciting process which gave me access to a lot of information about myself, over and above the eating problem.

I can change. I can decide. I can take charge. I eat food, food doesn't eat me. I don't feel guilty about my desire. I feel it but I don't feed it."

ANETTE

Taking Control

1. Since your addictive desire to eat is a product of your mind, it can only be dealt with by your mind. Physical solutions - drugs or changes in behaviour - will never be able to do this for you. In a nutshell, this is how to deal, mentally, with your addictive desire to eat:

⇥ **THE OUTLINE** ⇤

I have a desire to eat

I have the freedom to eat

Either:

I choose to eat addictively

Or:

I choose to accept my desire to eat in order
to gain the benefits of staying in control.

---

2. When was the last time you had a strong addictive desire to eat which you didn't satisfy, even though you could have?

3. Notice in what ways you benefit from using Times and Plans and the Outline. Make some notes about this. It's very likely you will take these benefits for granted later on and it will be helpful to have as much written down as you can - especially those benefits that have nothing to do with weight loss. These notes should enhance the list you made after reading Chapter Four.

4. Remember to keep all this to yourself. Take the full responsibility for what you are doing by telling no-one of your Times and Plans. If you don't bring the subject up you won't be inviting their involvement.

   Of course this applies to your day to day life, not to group meetings or therapy sessions which you attend in order to talk through these issues. There's a big difference between spending an hour or two discussing this technique with the help of a therapist or group, and bringing it into daily conversations with family or friends.

8 NO MORE FALSE HUNGER

In this chapter we take a brief diversion away from addictive thinking to look false hunger, a physical problem some people encounter that can make it difficult for them to eat less. Some people never feel false hunger, and some only start to feel it after they have cut down the amounts they eat. Their overeating was masking the problem, and eating more appropriate amounts of food brings the problem of false hunger to the surface.

There are two causes of false hunger:

STOMACH ACIDITY – Often misinterpreted as natural hunger, stomach acidity can be quite painful, so very understandably it makes it difficult for you to keep yourself from eating. Even the possibility of feeling hungry later on can drive you to overeat rather than risk feeling the pain of an empty acid stomach. I struggled with stomach acidity for some time so I know what I'm talking about. I overate a lot in an attempt to get rid of the pain.

Of course there are many kinds of antacid medication, but it's not a good idea to use it for a long time, so it's much better to learn what's causing the problem in the first place. Eating healthier food has proved to be the most effective solution for me, together with regular exercise and very occasionally a session of acupuncture.

As far as healthy eating goes, nutritionists advise us to balance 20% acid-forming foods - meat, poultry, fish, eggs, grains and cheese - with 80% alkaline-forming foods - most vegetables and fruits. Over-acidity can lead to serious problems such as ulcers and arthritis, so it's important to deal with this, quite apart from being able to eat less. (1)

LOW BLOOD GLUCOSE – The second cause of false hunger comes from the sudden rise and crash of blood sugar levels that results from eating carbohydrates which release insulin and glucose into the bloodstream too rapidly.

This connection between carbohydrates and insulin/glucose release is rated by the 'glycemic index' (GI).

Foods that carry a high glycemic index trigger an undesirably high insulin/glucose response. Foods that carry a low glycemic index cause insulin/glucose to be released at a slower rate,

GLYCEMIC INDEX OF COMMON CARBOHYDRATES

Insulin is released quickly by:

Grain-based foods
most breakfast cereals: corn flakes, museli,
shredded wheat, quick-cooking porridge oats
puffed rice, puffed wheat
white and whole wheat bread
white and brown rice, millet, cous cous
taco shells
rye and wheat crackers
pastry, croissants, cakes
muffins, waffles

Sugars
table sugar, glucose, maltose, honey

Vegetables and fruits
cooked parsnips, carrots, beet root, corn
potatoes (esp: baked, chips, microwave)
raisins, dates, figs, prunes
banana, mango, papaya, watermelon, pineapple
canned apricots, fruit cocktail

Snacks and drinks
popcorn, corn chips, puffed rice cakes
biscuits, shortbread
low fat ice cream, tofu frozen dessert
Mars bars, Lucozade, Fanta

Insulin is released moderately by:

Grain-based foods
white & whole wheat spaghetti and pasta
bulgur wheat

Sugars
lactose, sucrose

Vegetables and fruits
peas, baked beans
pinto and navy beans, canned kidney beans
sweet potato, oranges

Snacks and drinks
most chocolate bars
potato chips
orange juice

Insulin is released gradually by:

Grain-based foods
whole-grain rye bread
oats (whole, slow-cooking)
barley

Sugars
fructose

Dairy products
ice cream, yogurt
milk (whole and skimmed)

Vegetables and fruits
most green vegetables
soy beans, kidney beans, lima beans
lentils, black-eyed peas, chick peas
tomato soup
cherries, plums, pears, grapes, peaches
grapefruit, apples, applesauce
dried apricots

Snacks and drinks
pure chocolate
peanuts
apple juice (unsweetened)

For reference see: American Journal of Clinical Nutrition Vol 62 (1995) pages 871S-889S providing the body with a steady stream of energy and sustained mental alertness.

It's very important to understand that foods with a high glycemic index have a place in a healthy diet. The problem is that many of us have overemphasised these foods, eating too many of them too often. So simply eat less of the high GI foods, and if you are going to eat them, it's best to eat them together with low GI foods, to balance out the effects. Also, foods should not be regarded either as healthy or unhealthy on their glycemic index alone. It's just one factor of many, and certainly fat content should also be taken into consideration.

As well as creating false hunger, eating too many high GI carbohydrates is associated with a wide range of problems, including: low blood sugar (hypoglycemia, mood swings, headaches, dizziness), type II diabetes (hyperglycemia; it accounts for more than 90% of diabetics), difficulty losing excess body fat, fatigue, high blood pressure and heart disease.

Well-modulated insulin and glucose levels result in: reduction of body fat, no false hunger, increased and sustained energy, increased mental alertness, reduction of high blood pressure and cholesterol, increased cardiovascular fitness and less reliance on artificial stimulants such as caffeine and nicotine.

If false hunger is a problem for you and you take measures to eliminate it, you are just left with your addictive desire to eat. This desire, of course, is going to be easier to deal with when you aren't experiencing false hunger as well.

Even so, you are likely to come up with a host of reasons why you should feed your addictive desire, and this is the subject of our next two chapters.

WHAT PEOPLE SAY ABOUT *EATING LESS*

"Setting Times was easy enough, getting to them without eating was a lot easier when Gillian introduced me to the information about the glycemic index of carbohydrates. After a breakfast of even a huge bowl of cereal, I couldn't understand why I would get a gnawing hunger by mid-morning. The solution was so simple, though: soaked oats and fresh fruit have done the trick.

Now, any time I feel hungry sooner than I think I should, I think back to see what I last ate and it's always something with a high GI. So, I'm learning."

BETTY

Taking Control

1. I've kept this chapter short because these subjects are well covered in other books. If you want to learn more, I recommend you take a look at:

"The Zone" by Barry Sears (HarperCollins) which discusses in great detail the problems associated with elevated blood glucose levels and
"Gut Reaction" by Gudrun Jonsson (Vermilion) which is an excellent book on digestion in general.

9 YOUR REASONS WHY

Whenever we feel an addictive desire to eat, simultaneously we'll come up with a reason to satisfy it. The reason may flash through our minds faster than lightning, but it justifies our decision to eat: 'I'm going to go ahead and eat this because...' We may eat something because we'll enjoy it or because it will comfort us when we feel miserable. Or perhaps we think: '...I'd better finish it off before it goes bad.'

The addictive desire always wants to be satisfied, and our addicted minds will automatically select the most plausible reasons available at the time.

In order to take control of addictive eating, our aim first of all is to become aware of which reasons we are using. They tend to lurk at the back of our minds, not completely recognised. They encourage our addictive eating but when they are not fully acknowledged they are not brought out into the open for examination.

On examination, your reasons could be sound ones you wish to use, some might contain kernels of truth but be of questionable use at times, and some may serve no purpose at all other than to insist you satisfy your addictive desire.

You could call them reasons, justifications, explanations or excuses. You justify *how much* you are about to eat, *how often* you eat and the *quality* of what you eat. You don't need to judge these reasons as absolutely 'right' or 'wrong'. Some could be appropriate in some circumstances but not at all in others.

If you tend to eat more food than your body needs, this indicates that you have become *too attached to too many of these reasons too much of the time. So, instead of creating the results you want, you live with your reasons why you couldn't manage to do it.*

Simply discover which serve you best and which block your way. Awareness of what your reasons for eating are gives you the ability to choose them instead of having them choose you. Then *choose* which reasons you want to use, and aim to use them within the structure of Times and Plans.

It's essential to have some reason to justify eating! An anorexic may not accept any at all, even that of dying of malnutrition. But understand you don't *have to* eat in response to any of them. It's always your choice as to whether or not you satisfy any desire to eat, addictive or not. First of all identify a desire as addictive by using Times and Plans. *Then develop the habit of listening for the reason you are giving yourself for satisfying it.*

There are probably an infinite number of justifications for eating, limited only by your addicted mind's imagination - which is vast. Here are many of the typical reasons you may give yourself, with some thoughts as to how you might let go of them:

HABIT AND TRADITION – *I always eat eggs for breakfast, I always eat popcorn at the cinema, I always eat chips at this restaurant. It's the way I was brought up: I'm Italian so I eat pasta, I'm English so I eat meat and two veg, with Yorkshire pudding on Sundays. If it was good enough for my mother it's good enough for me. My family or partner expects it: we always eat pizza on Thursdays, my husband has to have meat and potatoes, we always finish a meal with something sweet. The clock: It's breakfast, lunch or dinner time.*

It is possible to eat according to your traditions within the structure of Times and Plans. It's also possible to recognise and accept the addictive desire which is triggered by a particular circumstance or time of day. Habit plays a significant role in any addiction. It's not the complete explanation for addiction, but it's a part of the picture. Those clients of mine who stop smoking experience their addictive desire in exactly the same way. For example, they feel their desire to smoke exactly at 5.30 as they leave their office, if it was their habit to smoke then.

In order to take control of your addictive eating, you don't need to change the routines with which it is associated. That will be impossible in some cases anyway, for example, if you buy chocolate bars at the corner shop on your way home - unless you move to the North Pole! Just expect to feel your addictive desire in those circumstances, especially at first, and it will help you to use the Outline.

By the way, notice that you are just as likely to justify feeding your addictive desire by something which is out of your normal routine such as a holiday, an unusual excursion or visit from a friend.

STRESS – *I always eat when I'm stressed - I've had such a hard day at work, I need to relax.*

Although created mainly in the mind, stress is, at least in part, a genuine physical problem so it's tempting to seek a physical remedy in overeating. However, far from alleviating the problem, addictive eating actually makes you more susceptible to the physical symptoms of stress. Not only that, but when you are stressed your digestive system is less efficient, so during stressful times it's wiser to eat lighter and more simple meals. Examples of effective solutions to stress are taking exercise and relaxation techniques such as yoga, meditation and autogenic training.

Now this is where you can really see the addiction at work, because the chances are you will not want to regard these as viable alternatives. Your addicted mind most likely latches on to the best reason to overeat, not the best reason for a visit to the gym! The difference between your level of interest in genuine solutions vs overeating could be seen as a measure of your addiction to food.

Remember it's always your choice: feed and reinforce your addiction or *acknowledge the addictive desire to eat triggered by symptoms of stress* - and devise new strategies that really do work.

PHYSICAL WELL-BEING – *I don't feel too well - I have a headache - I'm feeling cold.*

Any physical ailment, upset, ache or pain can act as a cue for an addictive desire, simply because in the past you have conditioned yourself to eat in response to such things. This does not necessarily mean that eating would be an appropriate response. All it may mean is you are experiencing your addictive desire again.

- *I'm constipated.* The best cure is not eating more but exercise and plenty of water - and to avoid the processed foods that create the problem in the first place. If you tend to suffer from constipation, notice which foods you have been eating, and learn by trial and error. Also, there are very good natural remedies, such as aloe vera juice or linseeds, available from health food shops.

- *I have PMS.* There is a connection between the food you eat and premenstrual syndrome, and a number of books and articles have been written on this. (1) You can choose food which alleviates the problem and eat it in a controlled way. This is quite different from feeding the addictive desire frequently associated with these times of the month.

- I'm tired and need a pick-me-up. This could be a very important reason to eat something - or it could be one of your favourite excuses for overeating. The way to tell the difference is to see whether you really do get more energy from eating, and this can only be learned by trial and error. If you feel dizzy or tired, and then perk up when you eat, this indicates you have been undereating. Either it's been way too long since you ate something, or what you last ate was of poor nutritional quality. (This is assuming you don't perk yourself up with artificial stimulants such as caffeine or chocolate).

If you sincerely suspect you have under eaten, eat something immediately. This is a valid reason to eat before your Time.

NATURAL HUNGER – *I'm starving - I'm genuinely hungry - I might get hungry later on.*

A feeling of emptiness in your stomach, natural hunger is one of the best reasons to eat, although it's not a reliable signal for everyone. Sometimes I eat when I'm naturally hungry and sometimes I don't. What's important is I don't fear it.

Your body isn't harmed by feeling hungry sometimes - it's only your addicted mind that objects. Natural hunger doesn't necessarily mean you are undereating, and some amount of natural hunger is actually beneficial to you because then your body isn't loaded down with food to digest. Digestion is one of the most demanding tasks your body performs, so natural hunger means your body is relaxing instead of being overworked and overloaded. Your body feels lighter and has more energy and vitality, your mind is more alert, and, because you're not overeating, your self-esteem is higher.

Natural hunger should be a pleasant and even enjoyable sensation which just comes and goes, and there should be nothing uncomfortable about it. It may be hard to believe at first, but in time, as you work through your addictive thinking, you can get to a point where you actually want to feel some natural hunger every day.

SOCIAL – *Everybody else is eating this and I want to join in - Eating is a way to be social - It would be rude not to accept it - I'll eat a lot to show it's appreciated.*

If getting other peoples' approval is the most important thing to you, you will be torn in two directions: compelled to join in and eat the same as others but, at the same time, concerned about whether you're looking slim enough. As you may already know, you can't possibly win!

Notice how often you let other people dictate the quality, quantity and frequency of your eating. At times it may be appropriate - but not *always*. It's essential for you to be able to say, at least sometimes: 'no thanks' or 'can I save it for later?' And it's important for you to be able to do that and feel OK about it. You can assert yourself in a polite and compassionate way, and other people may not be as offended as your addiction wants you to imagine.

Be aware, though, that others may unconsciously try to sabotage you. It's likely that the people around you eat addictively, and your addictive eating helps them to justify theirs. They may fear change in you, and not fully understand what's going on.

- I can only have a good time if I'm overeating. If you forget you are making choices and why you are making them you can feel miserable, envious and martyred if you are eating less than usual and/or less than everyone else. If you deal effectively with your addictive thinking you will enjoy staying in control of your eating, as well as enjoying the good company and the good food.

- I must eat it now while it's still available. This is like saying: 'I'll eat it now while I still can, because I won't be able to later.' So give yourself permission to eat whatever it is now and know that you will still have permission to eat it at any time in the future. If someone offers me something gorgeous, and I see eating it as addictive, it will help me to say 'no' if I allow myself the possibility of eating some later. If I still want it, I can include it or something like it, in my Plan tomorrow.

PLEASURE AND SATISFACTION – *It looks so good I have to have some - I enjoy my food - food is my hobby, my career and/or the love of my life - I deserve it - I won't feel satisfied unless I have more.*

Remember from Chapter Five that pleasure is an integral part of addiction. *The smoker, drug addict and alcoholic all pursue pleasure, and in doing so value it more highly than their health and self-esteem.* This is what you do too in your own way when you eat addictively.

As an overeater you have been confusing the appropriate pleasure and satisfaction that everybody gets from eating with the satisfaction of your addictive desire. For example, you get to the end of a huge meal and think: 'Now I'm satisfied!' This appears to be a very natural, reasonable response - and it is, in as much as you have satisfied your natural hunger. But your addictive appetite has also been satisfied, and this is more likely to be what you are referring to.

The tools of Times and Plans will help you to distinguish between your natural and addictive appetites. When you use the Outline to make fewer and fewer choices to feed the latter, you can derive enormous pleasure from eating in a guilt-free, controlled, non-addictive way, and this is entirely appropriate and consistent with the best possible health and self-esteem.

NUTRITION – *I haven't had enough protein/ vitamin C/ iron today - I don't know much about nutrition, so I'd better eat a lot to make sure I get enough.*

If you are that concerned about your health you have the best motivation there is to eat lower quantity and higher quality food. A substantial amount of research supports this. The way to improve your immune system, slow down the aging process and live a longer and healthier life is to choose a wide variety of foods that are the highest possible nutritional value - *and not to eat too much.* (2)

- *I'm pregnant so I'm eating for two.* It's possible that pregnancy will throw you off balance with your eating for all sorts of reasons. Take your doctors' advice as to how rapid your weight gain should be. If you are gaining too much weight too fast, it could simply be that you have discovered a new justification for addictive eating.

DENIAL – *It's just a little tiny bit - I eat less than my skinny friends - I have a very healthy diet.*

One of the most compelling reasons to overeat is to convince yourself that your overeating is not overeating at all. This kind of justification is common to all addictions, at least at some time in their development. Smokers say: 'I don't smoke very much so it doesn't affect my health.' Alcoholics say: 'I never drink alone, so I can't possibly have a problem.' It's one of the most powerful way for an addiction to justify itself.

Much of the research conducted on obesity is made more complicated because people who overeat tend to underestimate the amounts they have consumed. The overweight subjects are supposed to write down everything they eat in a day, but researchers discover the discrepancy when they compare these records with an analysis of urine samples which shows how many calories have in fact been consumed. It's entirely possible the subjects don't deliberately intend to mislead. They are simply in the habit of fooling themselves into believing they eat less and aren't even aware they are doing it. (3)

We can also delude ourselves into believing we eat the highest quality, healthy diet, when in fact we don't. Very often a few token adjustments are made - buying semi-skimmed milk, for example - and we use this to convince ourselves we eat wisely. Then this is used to justify satisfying any addictive desire: 'I normally eat such healthy food, a few biscuits won't make a difference.' Perhaps it won't - but do notice how frequently you use this justification to choose poor quality food. There have been times in the past when I've used it every day.

WASTE – *It's wrong to throw away food when there are so many hungry people in the world - Today is its 'best by' date, so I'd better finish it off now - I'll eat the leftovers, so they won't be wasted.*

But surely one of the most tragic examples of wasted food is overeating! There are people starving in this world, but eating addictively is hardly a solution. Throwing food away is a very constructive thing for you to do because it sends such a powerful message to your addiction: this is better off in the bin than in my stomach! It's only your addictive thinking that will tell you otherwise.

CONVENIENCE – *I don't have time to cook so I'll get my meal at M&S/ the chip shop/ the Indian take-away - I'm at the chip shop, so there's only fried foods to choose from.*

Your choices about what you are going to eat are made at least in part at the shop when you decide what to buy, and even in choosing which shop to go to. The same applies in choosing a restaurant because you know what you're likely to eat at each particular place, be it Chinese food, McDonalds or the pizza place with the salad bar.

Take note if you're justifying eating poor quality food by telling yourself you have limited options at the burger bar or that you don't have time to do any better. It's likely you are playing the 'Why Don't You, Yes But' game. Good quality food, fresh vegetables and fruit for example, is available if you really do intend to find it.

DOING BADLY – *I already blew it, so why not keep eating?*
This usually comes from years of dieting which creates the cycle of compliance and rebellion described in Chapter Six. You may find it difficult to take control back once you've given it up, but stopping at any point is always an improvement. Simply set a Time between 1 and 4 hours ahead. If feelings of deprivation and rebellion are common for you, study Chapter Six, working on the exercises at the end, especially the last one.

- *I'm too busy to deal with this - I've got so much to cope with in my life, I can't possibly think about dealing with my addiction as well.* It's crucial you tell yourself the truth: your overeating takes up time, thought and energy too. Making choices to accept your feeling of desire doesn't take a great deal of time, and some of your rewards will be greater alertness and feeling more on top of things in general.

DOING WELL – *I've lost some weight so it's OK to eat a bit more.*
This justification contributes to yo-yo dieting. If losing weight is your priority (perhaps the only reason you accept your addictive desire) then your motivation disappears along with the weight. So the more attached you are to weight loss, the more likely you are to put the weight back on! When you care less about your body size and shape, and more about the benefits you gain from higher self-esteem, especially from caring about your health as a preventative measure, staying in control of your eating will continue to motivate you.

- *I've been to the gym and burned off 268 calories so I can eat a Mars bar and still be ahead.* Counting calories means that weight loss is still your main motivation. Counting calories has nothing to do with taking control of addictive eating. Not only that, but counting calories doesn't necessarily have to do with weight, either, because this also depends on what kind of food the calories come from.

- *I've been so good I deserve it.* What you may really be saying is: 'I'm doing so well, I'd better screw it up.' If you have low self-esteem, success at anything will tend to feel unnatural, and you may get drawn into sabotaging yourself just so you feel 'your normal self' again. This is why it's so important to work on raising your self-esteem along with taking control of your eating. **It's crucial that you esteem yourself enough to be able to tolerate your success.**

- *I might become anorexic.* Anorexia and bulimia are characterised by very low self-esteem, a strong fear of weight gain, wildly out-of-control bingeing and starving, and an obsession with food and dieting. Some of you reading this book may identify with these, but not as a result of reading this book and using Times, Plans and the Outline. Long-term overeaters could not develop anorexia or bulimia simply as a result of learning how to take more responsibility by dealing with their addictive desire to eat.

When you apply this technique, the amounts you end up eating may seem alarmingly small - but only in comparison to what you used to eat. The truth is we don't need very much food in order to stay in good health, provided our food is of high quality. (4)

FALSE SELF-IDENTITY – *I am an overeater, therefore I overeat - I'm hopeless - I have no willpower.*

All of us tend to create false beliefs about ourselves - usually based on only one or two experiences at first - and then act in accordance with those beliefs over and over again, thus 'proving' their validity. When it comes to eating, it will help you to separate such beliefs from the truth.

For example, it may be true for you to say: 'I eat addictively at times', but when you make this mean something else: 'I have no willpower', that's *not* the truth. The truth here is more likely to be: 'right now I'm not using my willpower to take control of my addictive eating.' Addictive behaviour is *always* supported by lies. Telling the truth is *always* the way to take control.

Watch out especially for all those ways you describe yourself as inadequate. ***Your biggest obstacle to taking control of your eating could be your lack of belief in your ability to do it.*** This is usually rooted in convictions such as: 'I'm too old, fat, lazy, weak, self-indulgent, busy and/or stupid.'

Underlying beliefs such as these don't disappear in an instant, but it really will help you to remember that nothing about life is ever static. Change such as the one we are involved in here happens slowly, even imperceptibly. So, the first time you refuse to use your negative beliefs as a justification for overeating you probably won't experience anything like a life-enhancing transformation - but if you continue to do that, after time, that's exactly what you'll achieve!

PAST HURTS – *I overeat because of my unhappy childhood/ my parents divorce/ my divorce.*

Painful experiences in the past, an unhappy childhood or even a less-than-perfect childhood, often provide a constantly available justification for any addiction you choose. Most addicts tend to blame their past, claiming it's the reason they are the way they are today.

Alcoholics Anonymous tackles this issue by directing attention, not to the past injustice, which of course can never be changed, but to the alcoholic's continued resentment of the people involved. Begin to let go of your resentment, they advise, and you begin to heal yourself. Alcoholics who stay sober through AA don't need to approve of past hurts, just to forgive, and - crucial in this process - to refuse to use whatever happened as a justification for drinking.

After all, it's not the facts of what happened in your life that creates the problem - it's the fact that you use what happened to justify overeating. You have your explanation about why you overeat and you tell it to yourself over and over again: 'This and this and this happened to me in the past and that's why I'm eating again.' What matters *now* is how you are justifying your overeating *now*.

PRESENT UPSETS – *I'm feeling sad and if I eat something I'll feel better - Food is love - Food is a friend who comforts me.*

Also common, of course, is to use present time emotional upsets to justify addictive eating. Again, you are relating to food in the same way a drinker relates to alcohol, trying to use food as a way of coping with the difficulties in your life. Notice, though, that overeating doesn't really help you cope with your life. If anything, it makes life more difficult for you.

One way it makes life more difficult comes from the tendency to relate to feelings as a desire to eat and nothing else. This inevitably results in some degree of emotional dishonesty, when you pretend you're happy when you're not. In choosing to accept your addictive hunger you choose to sober up, you become more in touch with your true feelings and therefore more authentic. (5)

Whenever you feel upset and want to eat, you could spend some time simply allowing yourself to feel your feelings, asking yourself what you can learn from or do about this particular situation. It's that immediate, urgent addictive desire that gets triggered by your feelings that's the most beneficial to accept.

Another way addictive eating can make your emotional life more difficult is that poor nutrition - especially too much processed and refined food - is often an underlying *cause* of depression, stress and/or low energy. (6)

Also, notice just how miserable you need to feel in order to use feeling bad as a reason to eat. Is it simply the ups and downs of daily life? It's not that eating won't or shouldn't cheer you up sometimes, it's just that this easily becomes an excuse for any eating at all. It's one thing to feel comforted by a bowl of good soup when you're tired and hungry, but quite another to eat junk food all morning just because you woke up a bit grumpy.

I do not mean to trivialise painful emotions you may at times feel. It may be that you live with very difficult childhood or current issues that have not been properly expressed, dealt with and resolved. As I've indicated earlier in this chapter, the real solutions are usually not addictive so tend not to hold the same appeal. Therapy, a good recovery or personal development programme need cost no more than the amount of money and time you are currently spending on food you don't need. For some people they may form an important part of taking control of overeating.

Many people, of course, try to explain addictive eating entirely in terms of covering up negative emotions. But remember, our addicted minds automatically select the most plausible justification available, so a happy moment of success and celebration can become an equally compelling excuse to eat addictively.

If our actions were guided by our wanting to avoid feelings and nothing else, then going for a run does just as well. But most of us don't even think of physical exercise when we feel upset. I'm not suggesting it as a solution; my point is that whenever you feel strong emotions, you have *two* things happening: your feelings *and* your addictive desire to eat.

An addiction isn't just about avoiding unpleasant and unwanted feelings, it's also a strong attraction to particular sensory stimulations: the feeling of smoke in a smokers' throat or the sensation of chocolate in the mouth. Through repetition, a deep groove is worn in our minds to satisfy our desire for that sensation - and any relevant excuse will suffice.

If you happen to be on your own, the justification may be loneliness, but if you're with friends it will be politeness or peer pressure. If you've got too much to do it will be to ease stress, but if you're bored, you tell yourself you're eating to fill the time.

IF ONLY – *If only I had a different job... if only I had a man/woman in my life... if only I lived in my own flat... if only my family were less demanding... if only I had a different man/woman in my life... if only my life was more interesting... if only I lived in a different country...* then *I'd be able to take control of my addictive eating.*

Regrets about some aspects of life are often used to justify addictions. Any time you think about some circumstance in your life that you regret it's likely you'll feel your addictive desire to eat, through association, because you ate addictively in response to those thoughts in the past.

If what you want is a reason to procrastinate, you'll always be able to find one. Alternatively, you could take responsibility for one thing you can take complete responsibility for: what and how much you eat. Then, as a direct result you will be able to view the other circumstances in your life in a new way. Although many of these circumstances will depend at least partly on other people's actions - which you are not responsible for - you will be able to see more clearly what choices you have. And you will be motivated by higher self-esteem to take the actions that are required. But even if nothing else ever changes in your life, at least you will be in control of your overeating, and that's no small thing.

If your 'if only...' justification has anything to do with not having enough money, remember what happened to Ernie Bailey! He won £11M on the lottery and barely stopped eating, drinking and smoking until he died of a heart attack 20 months later weighing 22 stone. (7)

Addictions tend to persist, despite the circumstances. Taking control of addiction, despite the circumstances, is powerful and liberating - and could well be the only really effective strategy you can take.

FOLLOW YOUR ROUTINES

Assuming you don't win the lottery, my advice to you is not to make any other changes in your life in order to take control of your addictive eating. It's much more powerful to take control of your eating without making changes such as keeping extra busy, taking a holiday or avoiding certain people. This is because you can only break the hold of your justifications while in the relevant circumstances.

For example, if you eat addictively whenever you're bored, then you have developed an association between addictive eating and boredom. So, it's fair to assume that the next time you feel bored you'll want to eat.

My suggestion is that you allow yourself to feel bored just as you normally would. If you face and deal with your desire to eat and don't try to fill the time in any other way, you work on resolving the conflict presented by the addiction. Then, you are working through the problem by changing your priorities. You can only do that at the time it's happening, in those boring moments while you feel your desire to eat. You won't be able to think yourself through it ahead of time, only when you're there.

This is where you will make real progress; in those circumstances which provide you with your best excuses.

Many excuses, of course, are unavoidable anyway, especially those provided by our bodies. This is what we'll look at next.

WHAT PEOPLE SAY ABOUT EATING LESS

"Treating eating as an addiction was a difficult concept to grasp at first - after all, you have to eat a certain amount to live. But once you learn to recognise the addictive desire as separate from 'normal' eating, so many things fall into place.

All those excuses and justifications you've used for years fall away, and the simple acceptance that I EAT TOO MUCH is wonderfully liberating.

I now look at things like ice cream and chocolates and think 'I can eat that if I want to'. But now I am thinking about what I eat and getting into the habit of choosing the longer-term good of my body and self-esteem over the short-term moment of pleasure in the mouth - and it's a great feeling.

The technique of Times and Plans is especially useful for the evening meal, I find, as it keeps me from nibbling before and after dinner, when I'm preparing or clearing up. Instead of puddings, I now have a piece of fruit half way between dinner and bedtime, and really look forward to it."

MARGHERITA

Taking Control

1. If you have a tendency, as many people do, to call your overeating 'comfort eating' I suggest that you start to think of it as 'addictive eating'. Calling it simply comforting focuses on your perceived benefit only, which helps to justify it. It's much more honest to call it addictive eating (which may bring some sense of comfort). Satisfying any addictive desire can feel comforting but not always - and always at a cost.

2. Awareness brings you power. Make a note, mental or written, of the justifications you use. If you listen for it, you'll hear the reason you give yourself just as you are making the decision to eat.
   If you have difficulty figuring out what your justification is, just wait a while before eating until you know what it is. The longer you wait, the clearer your justification will become. Sometimes you might blank it out and go ahead and eat anyway. If this happens, discern the reason you gave yourself as soon as possible afterwards.

10 MY BODY MADE ME DO IT

In this chapter we'll look at the way people justify addictive eating by claiming some sort of problem with their body chemistry. These are all variations on similar themes, and they are all very common. It's true there is a biochemical side to any addiction, but now that scientists have more clearly identified what's going on it has become popular to think of addiction purely in terms of biochemistry.

PHYSICAL ADDICTION – *I'm physically addicted to food - My addictive desire is too much for me to cope with because it's a physical craving.*

Of course the food we eat has an effect on the chemical make-up of our bodies, and different foods affect us in different ways. For example, some food causes the release of extra hormones in the bloodstream, such as insulin and adrenaline, or the release of transmitters in the brain, such as serotonin.

It is possible that the less you eat foods which stimulate hormone or neurotransmitter production, the less your body chemistry will cause you to desire them - but don't ever expect to completely eliminate your addictive desire. It has a biological connection, but it is primarily created in your mind.

You can test this out in your own experience. Notice when, at least sometimes, you feel a strong addictive desire for things *for no other reason than that it's become available.* You walk past a certain shop, something enticing is offered to you unexpectedly, or you arrive home and remember the leftovers in the 'fridge. Notice when, at least sometimes, you feel completely satisfied only when you've eaten the last scrap of food on your plate, the last peanut in the bag or the last chocolate in the box - but not the second to last. ***It's your mind that has access to that information, not your body.***

When we think about hormones and neurotransmitters, it's easy to assume that biochemistry is running the show when it comes to addictive eating - but it's not. Whenever we satisfy our addictive desire we are trying to change our state of consciousness (i.e. what we are thinking and feeling). We hope to alter our state of consciousness to some degree, either just a little or very dramatically, and we use our biochemistry - our physical body - in order to do this.

But it is our mind that desires this effect, our mind that feels satisfied if the addictive desire is fed, and our mind that objects if it isn't. The addicted mind uses the body as a vehicle, but it's the mind that's in the driver's seat.

Addiction to food means you have conditioned your mind to expect certain effects - hopefully good feelings of comfort, contentment and satisfaction - as a result of eating addictively. When you're standing in the supermarket loading your trolley with chocolate biscuits and ice cream, it's your mind that's deciding you'll do that, not your body. It's your mind that decides you are going to go out and buy and eat more food in an addictive way, and it's only your mind that can take control of that behaviour by deliberately confronting the addictive desire.

Your addictive desire is automatic and inevitable because it lives on in your memory of having eaten addictively in the past. Time after time after time after time you thought to yourself: 'eat this and you'll feel better'. So you ate it and you felt better. You used your biochemistry to satisfy your addictive desire and to gain some sense of comfort and/or pleasure. Then, your mind remembers what happened and desires the same effects again.

You take control of an addiction by choosing to feel whatever you are feeling, instead of trying to change it. You choose to remain in your current state of consciousness, whatever it is, instead of seeking to alter it. By doing so, you refuse to accept that you are the victim of your biochemistry. *It's not your biochemistry that controls you, it's your belief that biochemistry controls you that undermines your ability to take control.* (1)

If biochemistry really has the last word, how would anyone ever take control of an addiction without chemical intervention? Yet it's done all the time, every day, all over the world. Alcoholics stop drinking. Heavy smokers stop smoking. And overeaters cut back on their addictive eating. Many achieve long term success, and the way it's done is by people sorting out their *thinking* not their *chemistry*. For example, they identify sound motivation and think about their problem in more conscious and responsible ways.

Smoking is widely thought of as a physical addiction, but I know from all the work I've done with smokers that the most intense and persistent cravings are *without exception* symptoms of deprivation, created by the denial of choice. With overeaters, feelings of deprivation result from a strong obsession with weight loss and lower levels of self-responsibility and self-esteem.

When you change your thinking by gaining acceptance of your addictive desire, you overcome your fear of it. From that place of acceptance it's then possible to alter your state of consciousness when you want to by other means, such as exercise, meditation and/or supportive conversation. If you are basically accepting your addictive desire, they won't be displacement activities and therefore won't become addictions themselves.

- I crave some foods because I'm allergic to them. Another physical explanation for addictive eating, an allergy is the body's immune response to something it thinks is a potential threat. The most common food allergies are thought to be dairy products and wheat, and it could be that you are allergic to these or other kinds of food.

However, an explanation of allergy on its own is insufficient unless it explains why an allergy to cats, for example, produces an aversion, when an allergy to wheat is said to produce an attraction. The connection between allergy and addiction is more likely to be that addictive eating - overeating certain favourite foods over a long period of time - creates an allergic reaction, rather than the other way around.

BODY WISDOM *– My body knows I need chocolate, bread, peanuts, bananas, etc.*

Yet another popular reason for overeating, this is a justification which claims a physical source but without reference to addiction. For example, a friend of mine was telling me that every so often she feels compelled to eat an unusual amount of French bread. She explains this to me by saying there must be some nutrient in this bread that her body needs, and so she feels 'a need' for it.

You too may use this reason to justify either the quality or the quantity of what you eat - but do you ever use 'body wisdom' as a reason *not* to eat something? After all, if your body is that wise, why doesn't it stop you overeating? I want to suggest to you that it doesn't do this because what you call your body's signal of nutritional need is more likely to be *your addictive desire to eat.*

A client of mine related a similar story to me, with the same explanation, with rice cakes in the place of the French bread. It's very interesting that both French bread and rice cakes have an extremely high 'glycemic index': they cause insulin to be released into the bloodstream very rapidly. (See table in Chapter Eight).

This a very common theme I encounter with clients, who often talk about listening to their body as if they are deciphering messages. Some books promote this idea too, suggesting, for example, that a desire for chocolate is your body's way of telling you that you need magnesium.

Now, if this system really worked nobody would ever become deficient in any nutrients. As soon as people were low in iron or calcium or whatever, they would immediately crave the food they needed and correct the problem. Perhaps people would even crave vitamin and mineral pills!

I'm not at all convinced that our bodies can send clear and reliable messages about what they need. If you are overweight or suffer from any diet-related illness, then it's self-evident you don't possess that intuition, or at least you are not in touch with it. Your body may know what it needs, *but that message can only be received via your mind, and your mind thinks addictively.* This means it will connive relentlessly in order to justify overeating.

There is, however, an entirely different way you might interpret the phrase 'listening to your body', and this is to observe physical states and sensations after having eaten. Are you lethargic and bloated or full of energy and vitality? The changes in these states might be quite subtle, but by all means keep noticing them and the foods associated with them. By all means pay attention to your body's excess weight, symptoms of ill health and low energy. In this sense, your body is clearly trying to tell you something important.

Remember too that people around you are probably also overeaters to some degree, so these things will apply to them as well. Just because they believe, for example, that chocolate is valuable in some way, doesn't necessarily make it true. (2)

Human beings survived for many thousands of years before such things were created. We don't need to fear the disease and famine which killed off our ancestors at an early age. We have our present-day epidemic of addiction to contend with.

JUSTIFYING WEIGHT – *I was born fat, it's just the way I am.*
Some people believe they just happen to be overweight no matter

what they do. This means they can avoid facing the reality of their overeating, which means they are less likely to consider how much they eat every day, and how much sugar, flour, fat and salt they consume as the real cause of their problem.

- I have a low metabolism - I put on weight if I just look at a piece of chocolate. According to a great deal of research into this issue, slim and overweight volunteers, fed the same restricted diet, all lose weight in an entirely predictable way. When energy intake is below energy requirements then - and only then - people lose weight. (3)

- My excess fat protects me from the world - My weight keeps me from getting unwanted attention from the opposite sex. Remember from Chapter Two that weight is an effect, not a cause of your problem. Imagine someone trying to justify smoking by claiming some advantage to spending each morning coughing! I hope you can see that smokers have developed an addictive desire for cigarettes, not for coughing. As an overeater, you have developed an addictive desire for food, not for weight.

After all, there are other ways to avoid unwanted attention from the opposite sex: wearing baggy, unfashionable clothing for example.

- It's middle-age spread. This could be true in part, but just a little part. Some experts say we can reasonably expect to gain about 5lbs for each decade after 20 - assuming we weren't overweight at 20, in which case we could lose weight as we age. We do need less and less food as we get older, so if we eat less, responding to our physical needs rather than our addiction, we will find that the all too common weight gain is not at all inevitable. (4)

- My mother was fat just like me, so it must be my genes. Of course we inherit many features from our family gene pool, but we still have our own choices about how we live. For example, we don't have to have the same political views as our parents nor the same taste in clothes.

Our genes dictate what part of our body our weight goes on, but our genes do not preside over our eating choices and therefore do not have the final word about how much weight we will carry. (5)

Genes are often blamed for all addictive behaviours, but the same principle applies. ***You may have been born with a genetic predisposition to become addicted, but you always have free choice*** *as to whether or not you will continue to satisfy and reinforce your addiction.*

IT'S YOUR CHOICE

And so we return to the theme of taking responsibility for our actions. When we don't take full responsibility ourselves, something else must be held responsible instead. Then, whatever that thing is, we have made ourselves victims of it.

As victims we complain: 'It wasn't me - I didn't do it!' and give the explanation: my body made me do it, my genes made me do it, my feelings made me do it, my mother made me do it, my father made me do it, my partner made me do it, my friends made me do it, my job made me do it, my addiction made me do it.

Then, instead of solving the problem, we get the perpetuation of the problem. It's so easy to blame other people or our circumstances for our own reluctance to change, but the reality is that each one of us is responsible for whether or not we take control of our addictive eating. We are only victims if we allow ourselves to be.

Childhood experiences have probably had an influence on this. Most of us are trained to respond only to the authority of others, rather than to listen to our own. It could well be that you grew up in an environment in which you were not encouraged to take responsibility for yourself, to whatever degree was appropriate for your age. Maybe you were told what to do far too much and weren't allowed to make many choices you could have made for yourself. For example, you may never have been asked what it was you wanted to eat for your meals, you may have been forced to eat things you really didn't want, and you may have been taught to regard food as a reward or an emotional crutch.

Even though you may have been raised in such a way - and many of us were - that doesn't mean you can't learn to take responsibility now. I imagine there are lots of things you've learned in your life that your parents didn't teach you!

It's no use waiting for responsibility to appear, thinking that when it does you'll put it to good use. Things don't work that way. Your breakthrough can only occur when you see that nothing will change now unless you make it change. There is never going to be somebody who just shows up in your life and solves this problem for you.

Set your priority on taking control of eating, rather than losing weight. Then, make choices to accept your addictive desire to eat, using the tools of Times, Plans and the Outline.

For example, you get upset about something that happens in your life and so your first inclination is to eat something to distract you from feeling angry and hurt (even though you may know that eating won't actually keep you from feeling angry and hurt). If you then go ahead and eat, you reinforce your addictive desire - but now you know how to do things differently. Don't expect your addictive desire not to be there. Instead, be willing to feel it, and know that by doing this you begin to break your addiction.

Then you simply face the problem life is bringing you, which you cope with more or less efficiently whether or not you are overeating.

Gaining an acceptance of your desire gives you control over your addictive eating, and as a direct result you free yourself from the despair of having food run your life. In time the difficulty diminishes as you work through the conflict and you get better and better at identifying and dealing with your desire.

You work on this every time you refuse to act on any of the reasons that justify your addictive eating.

WHAT PEOPLE SAY ABOUT *EATING LESS*

"Brought up in a family of overeaters, I had very high blood pressure and was very overweight. The doctor urged me to lose weight, but the mere idea of going on a diet made me feel hungry and eat more. Gillian's method has given me the insight to get my priorities right and to appreciate food for the beneficial effect it has on my health, both mentally and physically.

In the past I didn't give much thought about how I would end a meal and I would often end up gorging myself sick on bananas. Now, I remind myself that addiction thrives on confusion, so I make sure I have a very clear picture in my mind of what I need for optimum health, and by sticking to it I am keeping the addiction at bay. People comment on how much weight I've lost, but I know that the energy I've gained and my improved self-esteem are, by far, much more important than the lost fat."

JAVIER

Taking Control

1. Write down as many endings as you can to the phrase: 'I overeat because...' Don't censor them, just write down anything that comes to mind, however far-fetched it may seem. It's a powerful step to get them all written down where you can see them more clearly. Take a look at your list of reasons and choose which ones you really want to keep using and which ones you want to discard. You may discover a different range of reasons by trying variations on this exercise:

   'I eat because...' 'I eat junk food because...' 'I eat addictively because...' and 'I won't accept my addictive desire because...'

2. It's not necessary to make other changes in your life and in your personality as part of this process. In fact, it's very liberating to establish for yourself that you can take control of your overeating and still be far from perfect - as we all are.
   Taking control of eating doesn't automatically mean you will become more assertive, popular and clever, nor that you'll get a perfect marriage, exciting sex life or successful career. This may be disappointing, but it takes the pressure off, too!

11 ADDICTION AND SELF-ESTEEM

Now we have explored the three main aspects of psychological addiction, (responsibility in Chapter Six, addictive desire in Chapter Seven and justification in Chapters Nine and Ten) let's take a closer look at the relationship between addiction and self-esteem. To me, this is crucial because it's the exhilaration I feel when I have higher self-esteem *and nothing else* that keeps me going when the going gets tough. In fact, I think it only gets really tough at times when I've forgotten just how much my eating affects my self-esteem.

For self-esteem read happiness. It's what I feel when I wake up in the morning glad to be who I am, eager to tackle my day. It's easy to assume this depends on external circumstances - but have you noticed that your spirits can rise even though circumstances haven't changed in any significant way? Next time it happens, see if it could be the result of you having behaved recently in a way that reinforced one of the 'six pillars' of your self-esteem, as described in Chapter Four. For example, you asserted yourself in a new way, you took responsibility for something or you became more purposeful about getting something done. That's self-esteem in action.

When it comes to taking control of addictive eating, fully engaging with self-esteem as your motivation is a *major* change to be making. It's entirely possible you haven't made this change yet, so that losing weight is still by far the most important thing to you. Our culture encourages this, so it's not surprising, and it's likely you will be tempted down some false paths as a result.

One false path is found in substituting other behaviours. Often addictions themselves, these are likely to be things that don't contain many calories: cigarettes, chewing gum, diet sodas, coffee, tea, shopping, work and/or exercise. They may help you to keep your weight down, but they *don't* help you to control your addictive eating, and they *don't* support your genuine self-esteem. Any addictive behaviour will erode your self-esteem. Even more significant is your avoidance of your desire to eat, which means you don't take control of your overeating - you simply distract yourself or consume something else instead.

When weight loss is your goal, this kind of strategy makes sense - but you will never get to break your addiction to food this way. There are any number of things you can do instead of eating, but *if you are trying to control your eating through them*, you will still be out of control. You will achieve only a partial, conditional acceptance of your addictive desire to eat and therefore gain only a partial, temporary success.

This is especially true of smoking because it usually becomes such an all-day, every-day part of your life. You will only be able to deal properly with your overeating once you have stopped. If you are already an ex-smoker, be aware that your desire to smoke may surface when you cut back on your addictive eating. If you gained weight when you stopped smoking you substituted food for cigarettes. This means that your desire to smoke and your desire to eat will be interchangeable. (1)

[By the way, caffeine, tobacco and alcohol can cause the stomach to become too acid and stomach acidity can be misinterpreted as hunger, as explained in Chapter Eight. If you intend to continue their use, take this into consideration and be especially careful to include plenty of alkaline-forming foods in your diet].

Another false path is in using appetite suppressants, which are drugs designed specifically to eliminate your addictive desire to eat. For example, 'fen/phen', which were very popular in the United States a few years ago. The name comes from their composition: a combination of fenfluramine, which stimulates the production of serotonin in the brain but has the side effect of making people very sleepy, and phentermine, an amphetamine-like drug which counteracts the sleepiness.

People who take these drugs lose their interest in overeating because they feel satisfied with a lot less food. Their addictive desire has been taken away by the drug, and all that's left is a natural need for nutrition.

Although this may sound like the miracle cure we have all have been waiting for, this is far from the truth. After being available for years in the United States, 'fen/phen' has now been withdrawn due to dangerous side effects, especially damage to the heart. But they were officially approved, promoted as 'the most important weight-loss discovery of the century' and prescribed to thousands before their danger was recognised.

Apart from the side effects, you only get the effect of these kinds of drug while you're taking them. As soon as you stop taking 'fen/phen', for example, serotonin levels fall and stay low for weeks, possibly longer, and it's possible the serotonin receptors become permanently damaged and never return to normal. (2)

A belief in pharmaceutical solutions, so prevalent in our culture today, is often a feature of an overeating problem as it's another product of not taking responsibility. Any magic-bullet drug for obesity will have to be taken for life because there can never be a 'cure' for a behaviour such as overeating. Not only will they never work as instant 'cures', but remember that all prescription drugs have side effects; many of them are dangerous and some even fatal.

Using drugs is like going on a shopping spree with a credit card. You pay the bill later on but you still have to pay. Not only that, but when your addictive hunger does return you'll be less able to handle it because all the time you took the drugs you weren't exercising control of your addiction. You were just losing weight.

OIL AND WATER

I know it's difficult not to have weight loss - your appearance - as your main priority. Just continue to remind yourself that the real prize is the self-esteem you get when you take control of addictive eating. Losing weight is about wanting to make a superficial change in the way you look. Taking control of overeating is a profound change in the way you live and in what your values are. The more you think in terms of fat and thin, the more you are missing the boat. *I want to suggest to you that you will not lose weight - and keep it off - until you don't care about it as much as you care about your self-esteem.*

Like oil and water, these goals don't mix: *either* you set out to gain self-esteem *or* you set out to lose weight. For example, if you feel like eating before your Time, this doesn't necessarily directly affect your weight. You are unlikely to gain weight if you eat lunch at 12.45 instead of 1.00. When you care about your self-esteem, you wait to 1.00 simply because you said you would, which strengthens the power of your word to yourself, which is really all you need.

Other examples can be found in the self-deceptions that inevitably surround an addiction. Perhaps you eat food you told yourself you were buying for others. Or you eat food all at once which you had intended to last a week. Or you kid yourself you ate a healthy meal because there was spinach flavouring in your pasta.

When your goal is self-esteem, you start out by telling the truth to yourself because that's what matters most to you. Eating the same amount according to Times and Plans doesn't directly help you to lose weight, but it will strengthen the value of integrity with regard to food. Then, when that and the other 'six pillars' are in place when it comes to food, and especially when you prioritise taking responsibility for your health, weight loss will follow because then you will have the ability to take control - *and* you will have experienced the motivation which will keep you on track.

You will never gain self-esteem from eating addictively because, by definition, it's bad for your health. It's possible you don't fully acknowledge the cost to your health because your addiction wants you to ignore this. And it's especially easy to ignore because commercial interests in our culture encourage you to, and also because the effects on our health are usually so gradual.

Just as one cigarette doesn't give a smoker lung cancer, one biscuit won't make you diabetic, create a cancerous tumour or block your arteries. But smokers don't smoke just one cigarette and overeaters don't eat just one tiny scrap of fat or the occasional morsel of highly processed carbohydrates. *When you eat addictively, an entirely appropriate drop in self-esteem lets you know you're doing something that is self-destructive instead of life-enhancing.*

This is an essential survival mechanism: our own feedback system which lets us know how we're doing. We can't get rid of it and we shouldn't even try. Self-destructive behaviour gets a minus in the feedback loop. It says: 'This thing you're doing is harmful to your health.' Or it says: 'You've betrayed yourself again.'

Unfortunately, people who tend to have low self-esteem often exaggerate this into a completely unrealistic: 'I don't deserve to live!' and this is very unhelpful. Extreme guilt means you over-react to what you've done, which has the effect of invalidating the realistic feedback. If you are abusing your body, it's appropriate to think there's something wrong with that, but when it gets blown out of proportion by the unrealistic guilt, that's often ignored and therefore not acted on. (3)

Many overeaters try to ease their guilt by hanging on to the addict's typical philosophy of life: 'Life is for living, so eat, drink and be merry - we're all going to die one day anyway.' It may be that you are fully committed to this view of life, but it could also be that when you really think about it, you aren't so sure. Perhaps you think this from time to time, but only when it's convenient to because it eases your guilt about your addictive eating.

What happens to most people is they get 'wake-up calls' that cause them to question their 'life is for living' philosophy. A wake-up call may arrive in the news that someone their age just had a stroke. Or they are diagnosed as diabetic or as having high blood pressure. Or they get cancer or something that might be cancer. Then many, although by no means all, will drop the 'life is for living' philosophy and realise that life is for *living*! Then they start to make big changes in the way they eat, discovering willpower they never knew they had.

So why not pay closer attention to the wake-up calls and be more willing to act on them before they get too loud? It's only your addiction that's likely to object. You can find your very own, personalised wake-up calls in any symptoms of ill health you may have, and in your own experiences of lower self-esteem.

ACTING THE PART

High self-esteem isn't a luxury, it's a necessity. When it's missing we are more likely to experience periods of boredom, anxiety and even despair. We may try to avoid these feelings with a frantic schedule but will increasingly seek to comfort - or numb - ourselves in addictions such as overeating, getting to the point where we experience very little pleasure without them. But this only makes the problem worse by further undermining our self-esteem, leading us to find less and less pleasure in ourselves, and leaving us more likely to turn to addictions in an attempt to bring relief from our fundamental dislike of ourselves.

This vicious circle is most noticeable when we are alone, and low self-esteem often shows up as distress when alone with oneself. With nobody to distract us or to assure us of our worth, we are exposed to our own dissatisfaction with ourselves. As a result, most overeaters will eat addictively most often when they are alone. They don't want others to see how much they eat anyway, because other people's approval of them is always more important than their own.

This is the tragedy of low self-esteem: believing you're not valuable enough to stop overeating yourself into disease, premature aging and untimely death. If you find you cannot care enough about yourself to start to do things differently, at least you can 'fake it till you make it'. Pretend to honour yourself more, act accordingly, and the higher self-esteem will follow.

Acting accordingly means using Times, Plans and the Outline to strengthen the 'six pillars' of your self-esteem:

- You live more **consciously** by becoming aware of your addictive thinking: your desire to eat food you don't need and the ways in which you try to justify satisfying that desire.
- You gain **self-acceptance** as you accept the fact that as someone who is addicted you will continue to experience an addictive desire. Then, instead of resigning yourself to a life of uncontrollable overeating, you choose to accept your addictive desire when you feel it.
- You gain **self-responsibility** by reminding yourself that it's your choice whether or not you satisfy your addictive desire: you always have the freedom to eat anything you want, as much as you want. You take responsibility for your health when you make the healthiest possible choices, both in terms of quality and quantity.
- You stay in **integrity** when you keep your word to yourself by keeping to your Times and Plans, and when you spot the lies you tell yourself about what and how much you eat.
- You practise **self-assertion** when you say 'no thanks' to others, both in refusing food when it's appropriate and in refusing to prioritise looking a certain way in order to gain their approval.
- You live **purposefully** by consciously declaring your physical and emotional health as your primary goal, and set out, choice by choice, to achieve that goal.

NEW SIGNS OF SUCCESS

Perhaps all this sounds like far too much to remember, but really all you need to *do* is to switch your focus from how much you weigh to whether or not you are controlling your addictive eating. As with any goal you aim for, it's important to be able to check on how you're doing as you go along. Instead of seeing success in terms of getting into smaller size clothes, start to create a new standard of success:

- *Choosing Times and Plans, and keeping to them.* This brings you a real sense of control.
- *A more positive response to addictive hunger.* This is a sign you have shifted your motivation from weight to taking control. When weight is all you care about, there's no reason to accept the uncomfortable feeling of an unsatisfied addictive desire; you could avoid it and get the same result. When control of addiction is your aim, it makes perfect sense because this is exactly where your success lies.
- *A more positive response to natural hunger.* As a result you have more energy and feel lighter in your body instead of heavy from overeating. This is a sign you have worked through your addictive thinking, and taken more responsibility for your choices.
- *Better health and vitality.* This comes from eating less and making healthier choices about what you do eat.
- *Eating more of your food earlier in the day and less in the evenings.* Most addictive eating is done in the evening, which means you digest food when you are the least active, which is not good for your health. It's only when you have come to terms with your addictive desire to eat, which does tend to surface later in the day for most people, that you can start to correct the balance.
- *Staying off the scales.* This means you are developing your sense of self-worth based on your opinions of you, not on what other people think of you.
- *Keeping this process and any weight loss as private as possible.* This means you are doing this more for yourself, because you like feeling in control of your eating. When you discover that you can cope with the ups and downs of your life without overeating, this will mean far more to you than anything anybody else can ever say.

Taking Control

1. What might you currently be doing in order to avoid feeling your addictive desire to eat? Smoking, shopping or keeping yourself extra busy? Make a plan to deal with this so that you can gain more acceptance of your addictive desire. Remember, this is how you make real, lasting changes in your relationship with food.

2. Find out if you can, and if you don't already know, what diseases members of your family have suffered or died from. This will give you good clues to your genetic inheritance, and therefore what you are likely to be susceptible to. Then find out how diet affects these conditions. This will show you the foods which are especially dangerous for your health.

   Remember you will still have the choice to eat them. You will still experience a desire for them. And you will probably try to justify eating them.

   This applies just as much if members of your family have died as a result of addiction - to smoking, drinking or eating, for example. This indicates that you could have a genetic predisposition to become addicted, so the techniques and principles in this book will be even more valuable for you.

12 WHAT'S FOR DINNER?

How do you go about deciding what you are going to eat? Do you go for whatever it is that seems the most enjoyable to you? If so, how can you know whether or not your addictive desire is dictating what kind of food you choose? To take an extreme example of this, a person could eat very little in quantity, eat according to Times and Plans, but eat nothing but chocolate bars and crisps, which, I hope you agree, would still be an addictive way of eating.

Remember from Chapter Five that addictive eating is defined as eating anything other than what it is your body needs to stay in good health. As far as the quantity of your food goes, you now have Times and Plans to work with. In this chapter we'll take a look at quality. The highest quality would be food that meets your nutritional needs, and the lowest would be food that does nothing more than satisfy your addictive desire.

The more you move towards your nutritional needs and away from what your addiction desires, the more control you will gain. Of course, you'll need to know what your nutritional needs are so you can see when you're thinking about eating something you don't need. If you don't know the difference, you won't be able to identify your addictive desire so clearly.

So how can we be sure what our nutritional needs are? As I've said, I don't have much confidence in a natural instinct that tells me what I need or what I don't need to eat. I suspect that my addictive thinking has camouflaged any intuition I may have been born with. I'm not saying intuition doesn't exist nor that it is lost forever, just that at least for now I need to rely on the advice of others. If it was just up to me, I wouldn't have such insight into which foods were damaging my body until it was too late.

Fortunately I do have this information, and so do you. We know that people get ill and even die prematurely as a direct result of eating too much of certain kinds of food and not enough of other kinds. It happens gradually, but it happens and it continues to happen to an enormous number of people. It is possible that some of the information we are given about nutrition at the present time is incorrect, but the most responsible approach - and therefore the one that rewards us with the highest self-esteem - is to eat according to our best evaluation of the advice that's currently available.

There certainly is controversy in the field of nutrition; no two experts agree on every detail of the best possible diet. But to me, it is precisely this controversy that makes the overwhelming consensus of opinion on some things so compelling. When it comes to refined sugar, refined flour, salt and fat, there really is a great deal of agreement.

I've selected some passages from books and leaflets to give you an idea of what I'm talking about. As you read through these extracts, do remember that you choose what you eat; nobody is making you do anything against your will.

'Too much dietary fat not only causes an increase in body weight because fats are so high in calories but it is also associated with an increase in blood fat levels, which lead to fatty deposits in the blood vessels, especially those supplying the heart.'

(British Heart Foundation leaflet)

'...excessive fat and sugar content contributes to the accumulation of wastes in the tissues which impair proper cellular nutrition and encourage the formation of a kind of sludge in the bloodstream that can impede good circulation.'

(Kenton, *The New Ultrahealth*)

'Saturated fats are found in animal protein sources and in whole-fat dairy products... they tend to raise insulin levels by creating a condition known as insulin resistance.'

(Sears, *The Zone*)

'Throw out all oils other than olive oil... get rid of any margarine, solid vegetable shortenings and products (such as cookies and crackers) made with them.'

(Weil, *Eight Weeks to Optimum Health*)

'High temperature makes the oil oxidise so that, instead of being good for you, it generates harmful 'free radicals' in the body. Frying is therefore best avoided as much as possible, as is any form of burning or browning fat.'

(Holford, *The Optimum Nutrition Bible*)

'The eating habits of the population also play a significant part in the development and prevention of stroke, as blood pressure is affected by obesity, alcohol consumption and sodium (salt) intake.'

(Department of Health, *The Health Of The Nation*)

'The average western diet contains far too much salt, which causes edema (water retention) and also tends to deprive your body's tissues of oxygen... Fresh vegetables and grains and pulses have plenty of sodium chloride in them - all your body will ever need.'

(Kenton, *The New Ultrahealth*)

'The best choices... are always products derived from whole grains, such as whole grain breads and cereals. More of their nutritional value is intact, and they contain more fibre.'

(Greene and Winfrey, *Make The Connection*)

'Too little dietary fibre slows down the digestive processes, resulting in bowel disorders and constipation.'

(British Heart Foundation leaflet)

'...if you do eat unfavourable carbohydrates - especially bread - always use the whole-grain versions.'

(Sears, *The Zone*)

'Reduce consumption of white sugar and sweets in general. Diets high in sugar are most likely to be deficient in protective factors. Reduce consumption of packaged and highly processed foods, which are similarly deficient.'

(Weil, *Eight Weeks to Optimum Health*)

'Too many processed foods, prepacked, precooked, junk food, fast food - whatever they are, they contain too much animal fat, salt, additives and too little fibre.'

(Stoppard, *Woman To Woman*)

'We consume volumes of foods with a high level of phosphorus, which impedes absorption of good nutrients. Examples of these foods are soft drinks of low or normal calorie types, processed foods, canned, packaged, pre-packed, convenience foods and ready-made sauces.'

(Stewart, *No More PMS*)

'In the process of refining sugar, every vestige of life and nutrient is stripped from it. All the fibre, vitamins, minerals, everything is virtually removed, leaving only a deadly remnant.'

(Diamond, *Fit For Life*)

'In the primitive societies of developing countries, where people live on a diet of mostly unrefined carbohydrates, little or no sugar and very little fat, our common illnesses, from varicose veins and coronary heart disease to diverticular disease, are virtually unknown. That is, until a typical western diet, including white bread, sugary foods and so on, arrives. Then these illnesses begin rapidly to appear.'

(Kenton, *The New Ultrahealth*)

The chances are you are well aware of all this, and have already made changes in your eating in response to well-established and well-known health risks of certain foods. *However, if you are overweight or if you already suffer from diet-related illness, this is a good indication that you haven't yet made enough changes.* This is very common. The reason it's so common is because it's not enough to just have the advice, because even with all the advice and all the information - *you still have addictive thinking to deal with!*

This means you will experience your addictive desire - especially for refined sugar, refined flour, fats and salt. It is possible to eat many kinds of food in an addictive way (masses of apples, for example) but your addictive desire will be strongest for those foods with the most addictive qualities - and the chances are you will desire them every day, at every meal.

If I chose my food influenced *entirely* by my addictive desire, I'd only eat things like pizza, taramasalata, fried bread, sausages, cream pastries and chocolate covered raisins - to name but a few. I wouldn't eat fruit or green vegetables at all.

I'm not alone, of course. When it comes to choosing what to eat, many of my clients tell me they don't like fruit and they don't really fancy green vegetables - especially not every day, especially not raw, especially not without creamy dressings, and especially not as the main part of their diet.

This is all part of the addiction. When you are accustomed to feeding your addictive desire, you won't find nearly as much gratification in food which doesn't contain fat, salt or refined sugar and flour. *An apple just won't satisfy as much as an apple pie with custard will.*

Most of the time you choose between your nutritional needs and your addictive pleasures. Or you settle for a compromise somewhere in between the two. A nod in the direction of nutrition is often used to justify feeding the addiction again. For example, you'll eat steamed fresh broccoli - but only if it's covered in a creamy sauce. You order a side salad to start with - but just so you can kid yourself that your pizza lunch was a healthy one. You snack on fruit in the afternoon instead of something sugary - so you 'reward' yourself with biscuits later on.

As we saw in Chapter Five, your pleasurable responses to food are an aspect of your addiction. If your taste buds always have the last word, you will continue to eat addictively because they are, at least in part, the expression of your addictive desire.

It could be that you've made healthy changes in your diet up to the point where they come into conflict with your addictive desire. You've made some concessions, but continue to justify overeating fats, salt, refined sugar and refined flour in some form. Not only do you not need these because they don't supply you with essential nutrients, but the chances are you eat them in quantities that are actually dangerous to your health. *As far as your health is concerned, you'd be much better off without them.*

There is a great deal of processed, fatty and salty food available to us, and because it's food that has the most addictive quality to it, we are likely to be more attracted to it than anything else.

A good rule of thumb is: if it's advertised, it's likely to be addictive. Advertising costs a great deal of money, which means someone expects to make a great deal of money as a result, and, as any drug dealer knows, addictive substances are by far the easiest things to sell. This is why there's refined sugar and flour, fat and/or salt in almost all commercially prepared foods, and this is why people keep eating them. There is no other reason. (1)

Understand that there are people who design and produce 'food' (i.e. things to eat) guided by what will sell, not by a concern for your well-being. They care as little about your health as do the people in the tobacco industry.

What assists them in their marketing is the fact that so many people assume they are healthy if they are not hospitalised or because they don't have obvious signs of physical deterioration. This comes from having a standard of health based on more dramatic symptoms of illness. But just because you don't have a serious illness, this doesn't mean you are in the best possible state of health.

A serious illness is usually the final sign of a long-established state of ill health.

You can change your standard of health by paying attention to more subtle symptoms and finding out how the food you eat affects them. Do you ever feel tired after eating? Do you suffer from indigestion? Are you susceptible to infections? Do you have clogged sinuses? *These, and many more, are early warning signs that you are eating addictively much too often: too much in quantity and too little in quality.*

TAKE CARE

I do want to lodge a protest here and state that I don't particularly like this state of affairs. I know this sounds like my addiction talking, but I would prefer that pepperoni pizza was as good for my health as cabbage. I'd rather eat egg mayonnaise sandwiches than salad for lunch and I'd rather have crisps than pumpkin seeds for snacks.

Unfortunately it doesn't matter what I want, my body just isn't designed to work that way. It's like wanting to run my car on tap water: it doesn't matter how much I want it or how much I complain about it - it just doesn't work!

Whenever I fight against reality, it's me who gets the bruises. The more I fight it, the more bruised I get. The bruises in my case were acid indigestion, loss of energy and a very real dent in my self-esteem that I only became aware of when I started to make changes. The more wisely I eat, the better I feel - physically, mentally and emotionally. That's just how it is. You don't have to take my word for it, just check it out in your own experience.

You will need to take great care, though. The culture we live in tends to regard addictive food as normal, wholesome and even something to be highly prized. You will need to outwit the food industry, the slimming industry *and* your own addictive thinking:

Labels – Read labels if you don't already so that you know what you are eating. This doesn't necessarily mean standing in the supermarket studying every item before it goes into your trolley. You could read the labels at home and learn how to make wiser choices next time you shop.

Be aware, though, that the labels are often designed to deceive you:

-When the contents are listed per serving, take into consideration how many servings you really are likely to be eating when you buy the item.

- Ingredients must be listed in order of amounts used in the product, with the largest ingredient first. But there are ways of dividing the contents into two listings - two different kinds of sugar for example - so it appears to contain smaller amounts.

- Salt content is not clearly labelled at the present time. Sodium content needs to be multiplied by 2.5 to find the percentage of salt in a product.

- Be cautious of products labelled 'low fat'. All this means is there is less fat in this item than there would have been. Eating it doesn't necessarily mean you are eating a low-fat diet and it's easy to use the 'low fat' label to justify eating more of it than is good for you.

- The term 'refined' in describing sugar and flour is very misleading. The 'refining' process was developed for commercial reasons in order to prolong the shelf-life of food: these products have been 'killed' so they won't 'die' naturally in the shops. Far from being refined, they have been *destroyed*. (2)

CALORIES – Don't completely avoid foods just because of their calorie content as they may provide you with important nutrients. Peanuts, for example, are high in iron and vitamin E - and they don't have to be coated in oil and salt! Beans and lentils are good sources of minerals, fibre and B vitamins. Calorie content alone isn't a complete guide to what's best to eat.

ANTI-NUTRIENTS – Some foods have the effect of cancelling out other nutrients, so eating them is worse than eating 'empty calories', eating them contributes to a nutritional deficiency. This is very important, because many overeaters will choose something 'sensible' such as a salad, and follow it with a 'treat', such as a chocolate bar, cake or pastry. As far as your health goes, the 'treat' could be undoing the benefit of the salad.

Most manufactured foods contain anti-nutrients. Sugar, for example, provides no nutrition whatsoever, and depletes essential chromium and B vitamins. Most oils deplete vitamin E, and block the body's ability to absorb the oils we really do need. (3)

OILS AND AGING – I find it very helpful to remember that there can be a big difference between our *chronological* age and our *biological* age. In other words, the number of years since we were born doesn't necessarily relate to the condition of our body. For example, one very famous overeater, Elvis Presley, was said to have the arteries of a man twice his age. In his 40s when he died, he had over eaten so much his body reflected a biological age of 80.

The aging process is accelerated by an increase in the production of unstable molecules in our bodies called *free radicals*. The main source of free radical damage in our food is from oil: cooking oils, margerines and all the products made with them. That's why nutritionists are now recommending we only use small amounts of olive oil and/or butter, and fry seldom if at all.

Free radical damage is counteracted by the antioxidant nutrients, found in fruits, vegetables, whole grains, nuts and seeds.

BOOKS – There are many books on the market which explain the links between food and specific health problems, and good books on nutrition in general. If you don't already own some, most of my favourites are mentioned throughout this book.

Books on weight loss usually contain sound nutritional advice, but tend to reinforce improving your appearance as your priority. Even so, they provide many health-conscious ideas, such as ordering dressing on the side of a salad in a restaurant, using fresh lemon instead of salt, and stir-frying with flavoured vinegar or wine.

INCREASE QUALITY, DECREASE QUANTITY

It's no coincidence that we tend to overeat those foods that are the most damaging to our health. As we saw in Chapter Ten, these foods trigger chemical events in our bodies which, although they are not good for our bodies, feel good to our minds.

Those natural and positive responses we get from eating are simply exaggerated by overeating (too much in quantity) and by commercial processing (too little in quality). So we get more enjoyment and satisfaction than is good for us - which becomes both a result and a cause of addictive eating.

To make matters worse, we tend to think we aren't really allowed to eat these foods, which makes us want them more. We need to know we are free to do whatever we want, especially when it comes to what we do with our own bodies, so if we don't take responsibility for our own choices, we rebel by eating the 'forbidden' foods.

There's no other reason for these products to exist. A kind of collective denial in our culture makes them seem OK, but apart from satisfying our addiction, all those products *do* is make us ill. Addiction is the only reason they're eaten, which is the only reason they're bought, which is the only reason they're made in the first place.

This is important to see because making changes in what you eat could be as significant, if not even more significant, as making changes in how much you eat. Remember that you always have the choice either to satisfy or to accept your addictive desire for these kinds of food. Remember that by accepting your desire you gain in health and vitality. *Remember that there is also great pleasure to be found in high self-esteem.*

You don't need to completely eliminate your addictive eating, simply aim to do it less and less often. The more you gain an acceptance of your addictive desire, the easier this process will become.

When we eat 'as nature intended', both in terms of quality and quantity of food, we will look, feel and be our best. Even though what nature intends may not always be clear, a sincere and consistent effort in that direction will bring us far more rewards in terms of health and self-esteem than deciding it's all too confusing to bother with. Many overeaters remain ignorant and confused about nutrition just so they can continue to justify their addictive eating. (4)

Don't make the mistake of thinking, though, that when you decide to eat in a healthier way, that decision is made in a single moment. It's not. It's a decision that's made over and over and over again, every time you make a decision about food, every time you eat, every time you think about what to have for dinner.

You can take a break, though, when you go on a fast, and that's what we'll look at next.

WHAT PEOPLE SAY ABOUT *EATING LESS*

"After I had finished the Eating Less course I bought and read two books on nutrition: 'The Optimum Nutrition Bible' and 'Eight Weeks to Optimum Health' and started to eat according to those recommendations. I began with cutting out the bad fats, sugar, salt, refined flour, booze, caffeine, tea and any additives I could spot. Also chocolate, biscuits, cakes, etc. I drank water and watered-down fruit juices, herbal teas, and ate grains, pulses, fruit, vegetables, lean meat (only once a week) and fish.

I have introduced breakfast where none was before and settled down quite happily to three healthy meals a day which are satisfying and colourful. I've done a lot of research into organic foods and food products I had never heard of before, such as quinoa. That has been an interesting voyage of discovery which is not over yet.

It has been enjoyable and I expect it to continue to be so. I do not miss chocolate although I do miss cappuccino and Diet Coke.

I don't believe I would ever have been able to make these changes without learning what you teach in the Eating Less course. I am able to identify and understand my addictive thinking, and I am able to deal with it. This has provided me with the context for the changes I have made."

JUDITH

Taking Control

1. Notice whether you are about to eat food which satisfies your nutritional needs or your addictive desire. Your first and possibly your most important step is to tell the truth to yourself whenever you are about to eat food you don't need.
   You'll want to eat it, you'll be free to eat it, you'll try to justify eating it, and at least sometimes you will eat it. Just get into the habit of identifying it for what it is.

2. What is it about the quality of what you eat that you are most pleased with? What is it about the quality of what you eat that you most want to change?

3. Discover a new recipe and/or restaurant meal that you enjoy, making sure it's healthier in some way than you normally eat.

13 GYM AND TONIC

As we become more mindful about what goes into our bodies, we can also learn more about what needs to leave it. As you may know, poisonous substances enter our bodies every day. We can't prevent this from happening, and to some extent it's not a problem because we continuously filter out toxins and eliminate them. Our bodies do this automatically, just as our hearts beat with no need for our intervention.

In these modern times, though, we are often exposed to significant amounts of toxins from a wide range of sources: additives, preservatives and chemical residues in food and drink, exhaust fumes and other airborne pollution, 'recreational' drugs including alcohol, prescription drugs and tobacco smoke.

Some people experience extreme symptoms, but a great many people these days are suffering from some level of toxic overload without even realising it. Symptoms can develop such as: headaches, memory loss, weakness, depression, drowsiness, watery eyes, itchy nose, joint stiffness and muscle aches. When we continue to expose ourselves to so much toxicity and do little to counteract this, it's inevitable our health will suffer sooner or later.

So what can we do about it? First of all, we can avoid toxic chemicals as much as possible in the first place. As far as eating goes, the more you eat food close to it's natural state, the fewer additives and preservatives you consume. The more organic fruit, vegetables and grains you eat, the less chemical fertiliser and pesticide residue you consume. The less you eat factory-farmed meat and chicken, the fewer growth hormones, insecticides and antibiotics you consume.

We can also help to detoxify our bodies by taking exercise and by fasting.

EXERCISE

Exercise assists in detoxification, and it also plays a part in taking control of addictive eating. This is because much of your motivation to stay in control will depend on how good you feel physically. Eliminating the nausea, bloating and lethargy which come from overeating may well provide you with your strongest incentive to continue to make different choices. The more fit you are, the stronger this motivation becomes and the more likely you are to notice and respond to more subtle changes in energy.

Most importantly, though, exercise of any kind helps to detoxify your body by increasing the amount of oxygen circulating in every cell and in every major organ. Moving the outside of your body gets everything moving on the inside, flowing as it's supposed to do: circulatory system, lymph system, digestive system and the rest. *It quite literally makes your body younger because it counteracts all the aging processes*. It brings you more energy, less stress, and as for your mind, is one of the best treatments for depression. (1)

However - as many people know only too well - the problem with exercise is that the vast majority of those who take up some form of exercise put it down again within a short space of time. Boredom is usually given as the explanation. If you are one of those who start but then stop exercising, and if you think the reason for this is boredom, it may help you to consider a different explanation.

When you think about it, there are plenty of things we do each day which don't provide us with challenging intellectual stimulation. Any daily routine can be boring, but we do them because we are motivated to do them, and we are motivated because we gain in some way.

So too can any exercise routine become boring, but the reason it's abandoned isn't boredom, it's *resistance*. This resistance is the gravitational pull of inertia - the tendency of matter to remain at rest unless affected by an outside force - and it's experienced in direct proportion to the amount of effort required.

Resistance shows up as an objection to the prospect of taking exercise, when you 'get too busy' or decide you'd rather visit the pub or watch TV. Resistance can also show up as feeling too tired, and although this looks like the perfect excuse to sit down and rest, notice that when you go ahead and exercise anyway, your energy *increases* as a result.

The point is that you should always expect to have resistance. It's a big mistake to think that one day unbridled enthusiasm for exercise will suddenly appear on your doorstep. Here are some suggestions to get and keep you going:

REDEFINE – Just as the word 'dinner' could mean a hundred different things to a hundred different people, so can the word 'exercise'. Unfortunately, many people have an extremely narrow definition, which usually includes pain, exhaustion and scanty leotards.

Define exercise as moving your body, as distinct from being still. All you need to do is to simply - and slowly - increase the amount of exercise you do. It can actually be dangerous to increase exercise too rapidly because it puts too much strain on your body. And you're much more likely to give up on it all together. By all means push yourself up to your limits, but never beyond them.

Anything - a half hour walk on a Sunday afternoon or using stairs instead of a lift - is better than *nothing*. The key is in making sure the exercise suits your body and your level of fitness. Some form of exercise is usually possible, even for those with bad backs, those confined to a wheelchair and for the elderly.

MOTIVATE – As with motivation to eat less, motivation to exercise is much more effective if you think of it as taking responsibility for your emotional and physical well-being, instead of purely as a way to change the shape of your body.

I find I am more likely to keep exercising regularly when I regard it as the way for me to release toxins, stress and negative feelings such as anger and frustration - all of which are quite literally stored in our bodies and pose a genuine threat to health. I stay motivated to exercise because I experience tangible rewards immediately following exercise. I feel much more positive about everything, I have more energy, I sleep better, I feel more relaxed and my digestive system improves. I also notice greater clarity of thought and find I come up with wonderful solutions to all kinds of problems while at the gym.

VARY – Walking is said to be the best form of exercise because it has the lowest risk of injury and it gets your heart and your lungs working. You'll get the best results if you stride out and keep up a brisk pace for as long as you can, ending up slightly out of breath but not gasping for air. Toxins are stored in fat cells, and fat mostly gets burned off after you've done about 20 minutes of exercise, so walk for half an hour or more to get the benefit.

Find exercise you enjoy and any time you begin to feel fed up with it, do something else for a while. Some people enjoy the competition involved in sports, for others exercise is a chance to connect with the natural world of trees, birds and sky. Sometimes this is what exercise brings to my life, and sometimes I take my Walkman to the gym and look forward to listening to my favourite music. If I get 'bored' all I need to do is find another tape to play.

For me, though, it isn't boredom, it's resistance, and nine times out of ten, as I pick up my gym bag and put on my trainers, I think to myself that I'd rather do something less energetic instead. I suppose there are people to whom exercise comes easily and naturally, but I am certainly not one of them. Once at the gym, though, I do enjoy myself and afterwards I'm *always* glad I didn't give in to my resistance.

FASTING

Even if you haven't the slightest intention of ever going on a fast, do read this section. Fasting is not an essential part of this technique, but if you read about it you may begin to see fasting in a new light, and there are some details about addictive eating you may find helpful.

Fasting can help you in two ways. It promotes health because it helps to detoxify the body and, if done correctly, it can help you to work through your addictive thinking.

If I mention to people that I fast, their reaction is often one of serious concern for my well-being. Let me assure you, I am, like most of us in the western world, a long, long way from starving. Anybody who overeats would stay alive for at least a month on stored body fat alone. Overeaters problems are much more likely to be caused by too much food rather than too little.

It may be that anorexia and bulimia have given fasting a bad name. Fasting in itself is not a dangerous thing to do. Millions of people fast for either health or religious reasons with no detrimental effects at all. Fasting only becomes a problem when it's done for the wrong reason: an extreme attachment to weight loss. When someone starts to fast because they are desperate to lose weight, it certainly can become a very real problem. The problem isn't with the fasting, though. The problem is the deadly combination of fasting and believing that your life - and your self-esteem, which can feel like the same thing - depends on looking acceptable to other people.

Fasting, if done correctly, has an entirely beneficial effect on your physical health. As the authors of the book *Fit For Life* say:

'We eat and live in such a way as to never allow the insides of our bodies to be cleansed sufficiently, and that is why 62 percent of the population of this country is overweight. It is also a contributing factor to the fact that three out of four people in this country will develop some form of heart disease or cancer in their lifetime. The outside of the body is washed, but the inside, which is far more important, is not washed. I'm talking about some people going for decades, their entire lives, without ever doing what is necessary to wash out the toxic waste from inside their bodies.'

So there are very good reasons to go on a detoxification fast. However, for some people there may be even better reasons not to fast, and it will be important for you to take these into consideration in order to decide what's right for you.

GOOD REASONS NOT TO FAST

- *It's not a good idea to fast* if you are desperate to lose weight or if you have a history of anorexia or bulimia. A detoxification fast could result in some weight loss, but fasting isn't the best way to lose weight anyway, because, as you probably know, your metabolism slows down when you don't eat for long periods of time.
- *It's not a good idea to fast* if you have a tendency to overeat either before or after a fast. As we discussed in Chapter Six, this is a rebellious reaction to the denial of choice, which indicates you are not taking as much responsibility as you could. You'd be better off spending more time with Chapter Six, especially the exercises at the end, before you start to fast. Get used to reminding yourself that you've always got choices, and then take a few short fasts to see how you react.
- *It's not a good idea to fast* if you go on a fast as a way to take control of your overeating. In other words, if you do a lot of addictive eating, you start to feel disgusted with yourself, and so you fast in order to feel better about yourself. This tends to create an 'all or nothing' attitude towards food, where you are either overeating or fasting. Then whichever of these states

you are in, it reinforces the other one.

People who spend most of their time either fasting or overeating aren't spending much of their time practising control, especially facing that strong addictive desire which gets triggered by eating. The best way to take control of your eating is by setting Times, making Plans and using the Outline.

- *It's not a good idea to fast* if you are not in the best of health, if you're coming down with something or recovering from it, or if you suffer from a condition such as diabetes or hypoglycemia. It's always wise to get your doctor's advice if you have any concerns about the effect fasting may have on your state of health.
- *It's not a good idea to fast* if you don't normally eat a high quality diet at other times. If you normally eat the kind of poor quality food described in Chapter Ten and then you fast, it's very likely you won't be providing your body with the nourishment it needs.

Not only that but you'll probably experience unpleasant physical withdrawal symptoms. These are symptoms of detoxification and I realise that this is the point of the exercise, but if you end up with things such as bad headaches and dizziness you may not want to fast ever again. When you improve the quality of your diet, these symptoms won't appear when you fast.

HOW TO FAST NON-ADDICTIVELY

There are many different ways of fasting. A fast can be as short as a night's sleep (that's why we call it breakfast!) or last many days. You can fast by eating just one kind of food - usually recommended are fruit such as apples or grapes - or you can fast by just drinking liquids and eating no solid food at all.

The published detoxification plans include fruit, sometimes vegetables, and usually cover a week or more, and it may be that it suits you to take the time once or twice a year to do a longer fast. However, if this seems a bit too long for you it could put you off the idea completely. Personally, I find that a discipline of fasting for 24 hours once a week is very beneficial both to my physical health and my addictive thinking.

I fast either by drinking liquids only, or sometimes by eating fresh fruit only, for 24 hours, from one evening to the next. For example, from 6pm to 6pm the following day. I choose different days of the week depending on any social plans I may have. I don't do this continuously, but I return to it as a weekly practice because I enjoy it and find great benefit in it.

The best purpose of a fast is to remove toxins from your body and to help you to gain control of your addiction. If it's not done correctly, it could reinforce your addiction by encouraging feelings of deprivation and negative reactions to addictive and natural hungers. So if you are going to fast, it's important to do it in a way that deals positively and effectively with your addictive thinking, rather than in a way that reinforces it.

Here are my suggestions:

- Determine what kind of fast you are going to go on and how long it will last before you begin. Set a Time just as you normally would, the Time being when you say you are going to end your fast. The addicted mind thrives on confusion, so it's important to set clear goals. It wouldn't be so good to decide to fast only after realising you happen to have not eaten for a rather long time. In the same way, it isn't a good idea to start a liquids-only fast and half-way through decide to eat fruit - unless you have a genuine concern for your health, such as feeling faint.
- Set Times and Plans for the fruit if you think you may eat it addictively.
- Fruit is best eaten raw because it contains all the enzymes which detoxify your system. Most fruit juices, though, produce excess insulin so it may be better to avoid them.
- Drink water, bottled or filtered, as you normally would. At least 8 glasses a day is usually recommended.
- For a liquid fast, I take the amount of money I would have spent on food and splash out on high quality, high nutrition alternatives, available from most health food shops:
    - organic vegetable juices and broth
    - miso soup
    - green drink
    - protein/carbohydrate drink

It's very unlikely you'll feel weak or tired with all that, but if you do, drink one of these immediately.

- I don't set Times and Plans for these drinks, but by all means do so if you want to, so that you don't drink addictively, simply replacing drinks for addictive eating. A bad taste in your mouth is a sign the toxins are coming out, and you may want to use a mouthwash.
- Coffee, tea, alcoholic drinks and commercial fizzy drinks are counter-productive because they contain toxins and because they are likely to create an acidic stomach in the absence of solid food. Drink them very little, if at all.
- If you are new to fasting, try 8 hours at first. 24 hours once a week is probably the maximum amount to do. Fasts can be relatively easy because while you are fasting you are not making such challenging eating choices.
- Fasting gives you a very good opportunity to pay attention to your experiences of addictive and natural hungers, and to work on gaining an acceptance of them. It's best not to drink when you feel a strong addictive desire to eat so that you can use the Outline and make a clear choice to accept it.

  You will notice that your natural hunger comes and goes, and that it's possible to experience natural hunger without any addictive hunger. It's also possible to experience addictive hunger (your addictive desire to eat) without any natural hunger. And it's possible to experience both at the same time.
- During your fast, go about your business as you normally would for the day. I fast at the same time as I live my life as usual, and it's very important to me to be able to do that. I find I have plenty of energy for a work-out at the gym, even towards the end of a 24 hour fast. Fasting in this way helps you to lessen the grip of many justifications for overeating, because you see in your own experience that you really can live your life going for longer periods of time with no food at all.
- Fasting also provides you with an opportunity to work through any feelings of deprivation. In order to do this, keep reminding yourself that you always have choices, and keep making your choices in the present time, both before and during the fast.

  You may notice you've projected into the future as soon as you begin a fast, thinking: 'Now I can't eat anything for the next 24 hours!!' Aim to fast for 24 hours (or whatever you've chosen) but realise you can only accomplish this by making choices in each moment as it comes.

You are likely to experience symptoms of deprivation if you don't train yourself to make all your choices in the here and now. Just remind yourself that you cannot choose to eat or not to eat in the future. Choices only function in the present time - at the moment you make them. Otherwise, they cease to be genuine choices!

- Before you begin your fast, eat lightly, or at least no more than you normally would. Otherwise you are trying not to feel your hunger - or more likely not to feel deprived - for the duration of the fast. This usually comes from the fear: 'I won't be able to eat for a long time, so I'd better eat as much as I can now.' Remind yourself that nobody's making you do this. If you are fasting, it's your choice. If you are hungry, it's your choice. If you are feeling an addictive desire to eat, it's your choice.

A fast can be a very positive experience. Staying in the present time and choosing it moment by moment makes all the difference. If you do this you will see that fasting can be an enjoyable thing to do, that it's very satisfying and even exhilarating. You will see for yourself how energised your body feels and this is an invaluable experience for you in breaking your addiction to food.

For me, though, the exhilaration I feel mostly comes from a tremendous sense of accomplishment from taking on such a challenge.

WHAT PEOPLE SAY ABOUT *EATING LESS*

"Fasting is the area of the book I felt most resistant to - I just didn't want it to be true. It made good sense though, so eventually I decided to give it a go.

My first attempt was a 24-hour fast from 7pm Friday night to 7pm Saturday night. I booked it in my diary several weeks before and it helped me to eat high quality food and less quantity in the lead up because I knew that the more 'poison' there was in my body the harder it was going to be. I also planned my last meal and first meal very carefully to reduce the risk of panic eating.

During the fast all I consumed was water and some organic vegetable juice (which I thought was disgusting!) I went to the supermarket, did a hard session of aerobics, went shopping in central London with a friend, had a lively afternoon visiting family and then went to the cinema. The worst bit was the last four hours. I developed a bad headache and had an incredibly strong desire to eat.

Fasting has given me an extra tool I can use. When the voice of my addictive desire shouts: 'I'm hungry; you must feed me now', I can reply: 'Don't be stupid, if I can go for 24 hours without eating, I can certainly make it for four.'

Does fasting have long-term benefits for my health? I don't know. Does it make me feel good about myself? Absolutely."

KATIE

Taking Control

1. If you don't already exercise at least four times a week, discover and try out a new form of exercise that you enjoy.

2. Look for opportunities every day where you can walk instead of taking a car, bus, lift or escalator.

3. If you are ready to take another step towards taking control and enhancing your health and vitality, set a date and a time for a fast. Make sure you know what you are going to be consuming over the fast, and that it's available.

14 EATING FOR YOUR LIFE

Times, Plans and the Outline are tools for you to use, and just like any other tool their purpose is to make the job easier. After all, you might be able to get a nail into a piece of wood without a hammer, but if you have a hammer why would you bother to try?

Like any other tool, they don't do the job for you; they only work when you use them. And, like most tools, it may take you a while to get used to them, so at first they may feel awkward, requiring some effort and concentration.

When I say these tools make the job easier, 'the job' in this case is accepting your addictive desire to eat. By using these tools you can make this acceptance real to you as a functioning part of your life, thereby transforming your relationship with food. Gradually it becomes a part of your thinking, it becomes something you own.

This desire isn't going to go away, so all you can do is either satisfy it or accept it. (You can also avoid it, but only temporarily). Gaining an acceptance of it isn't accomplished instantaneously. The Outline provides you with a structured thought process which enables you to gain this acceptance by weighing up the choices open to you. This is a process which evolves over time.

When you don't use the Outline - and it needs to be used deliberately and consciously - your addictive thinking takes over by default. This means you're likely to react as if you don't have a choice, you'll resent and resist the desire and forget your motivation to accept it.

Any addiction tends to create 'selective memory' *especially while you are feeling your addictive desire.* This means you are likely to remember only the good things about satisfying it and forget the bad consequences - until later on, when the desire is satisfied and you remember and regret what you've done. Your deliberate use of the Outline counteracts this selective memory.

The real challenge may be in spotting your addictive desire in the first place; Times and Plans make it much easier to see.

THE OUTLINE (SEE PAGE 84)

Step 1 'I have a desire to eat' First of all, you acknowledge that you have an addictive desire, and remember it's inevitable simply because you have eaten addictively in the past.

Step 2 'I have the freedom to eat' When you acknowledge the fact that you've got a choice, you'll be able to make one. You get yourself to see that it's your choice to take control. Then, *and only then,* you are neither complying nor rebelling: you are taking responsibility.

Step 3 'I choose to accept my addictive desire…' This is the most important step. Remember, the only reason you have not had control in the past is that you have not been willing to experience the uncomfortable feeling of an unsatisfied addictive desire to eat. By choosing to accept it you turn it into a positive experience and gain control.

Step 4 '…to gain the benefits of…' You break free from an addiction by resolving the conflict you are in about it. You do this by choosing to feel your addictive desire because it's worth it to you, because of whatever it is that you get as a result of taking control of your overeating. It may help if you have something about this written down somewhere because your addicted mind may tend to forget these benefits - especially those benefits other than losing weight.

IN AND OUT OF CONTROL

The great majority of my clients are delighted when first introduced to this technique. They set Times, make Plans and experience real benefits as a result. They feel in control of their eating, often for the first time in years. They have more energy, feel healthier and esteem themselves more highly.

Sooner or later, though, as you might expect, their enthusiasm begins to fade. At some point they stop setting Times and eat beyond their Plans. They eat addictively more and more often, and then begin to wonder what went wrong.

It could well be that you have a similar experience. Maybe you've already started to use these techniques, and although you find them helpful when you use them, you don't use them often enough or strongly suspect that it's just a matter of time before you lose interest in them.

It will help you to know that going through periods of time when you don't use these techniques is to be expected. I never assume that anyone, including myself, will use these techniques consistently each and every time they eat, every day for the rest of their lives. Not only is this an extremely unrealistic expectation, it's also a dangerous one.

The fact is that taking control of addictive eating is a long-term process, and there will be lots of ups and downs along the way. This may sound discouraging, but if you don't acknowledge this, you are more likely to get hopeless about it when you do go out of control, so that you don't want to use the technique ever again. However, if you understand that it's inevitable you'll lose control at some point, then when you do, you realise that all you need to do is to get back on track. You see, it's not losing control that gives you the problem, it's believing that this shouldn't ever happen.

While you use this technique, even if it's just for a limited period of time, you can't help but discover more about your addictive eating. If you just continue to gain more and more insight into your addiction and what's running it, that's all you need to get the job done. The only reason you wouldn't get good results in the long term is if you completely give up your involvement with this process - *and one of the main reasons people give up is they expect too much of themselves too soon.*

Taking control of addictive eating requires a steady process of growing awareness. Awareness regarding what food you really do need to stay healthy - and what you don't need - and awareness of your own addictive thinking and the tricks it plays.

The first time you get back into control may well be the most significant because this is when you establish for yourself that you *can* get back into control. Then, all you need to do is to develop the ability to get back on track faster.

In time, you will find that you are able to increase the quality and decrease the quantity of what you eat during those times you are out of control. The idea is to take what may be a roller-coaster ride of variation between 'out of control' eating and 'in control' eating and flatten it out so it's more like a bumpy road. When you end up with 'out of control' eating that's not very different from your 'in control' eating, that's when you'll feel much more relaxed and confident about the whole business.

This confidence is something I hear about from my clients, even a long time after they've done my course. Nobody is following the technique perfectly, but in general there's a undeniable improvement in their eating, both in quality and quantity.

Here are some thoughts about staying in touch with this process in the long term. They may be especially helpful to read when you've 'lost it':

- *A process of taking more responsibility.* You could find things go well at first simply because you are 'being good' by complying with what you regard as a new set of rules and regulations - Times and Plans - just as you may have complied with countless diets in the past. Although compliance looks like you're succeeding, it will lead to rebellion sooner or later.

  You don't need to worry about figuring out whether or not you're complying. If you are, all that will happen is that at some point you'll start to get rebellious - and that's when you really can start to make progress. At this point you'll begin to feel deprived and then begin to eat more addictively, probably latching on to some compelling justification you've just discovered.

  Your tendency not to take responsibility for your eating choices was there before you read this book: the technique simply helps you to notice it. The technique then provides you with a way to work through it by connecting with your free choices and what those choices mean to you, as described in Chapter Six.

  While you are not taking as much responsibility as you could, you may eat a lot of 'forbidden' foods before you really believe you are free to eat them. As a result you will undoubtedly be consuming far too much salt, fat and refined products than is good for your health. Just work on eating these kinds of food less often. In order to do this, simply choose to accept your desire for them more often, always making your choices in the present time.

- *A process of meeting different aspects of your addiction.* Some of your more compelling feelings of desire, and your more convincing justifications for satisfying it, may surface long after starting to work with the technique. This is especially likely to happen if you've done a lot of dieting in the past, when you've trained yourself to repress your addictive desire to eat for periods of time. As a result you could get the impression that this is a lot easier than it actually is, and again, it's only when things start to get more difficult that you can make real progress.

  Here's an example of what I mean. I had been counselling Sarah for about six weeks when she explained to me that she was not at all in control of her eating, and couldn't possibly take control because her work schedule was far too demanding for her to spend time thinking about Times and Plans. Prior to this she had been using the technique for well over a month and was very pleased with the results. When we started to talk about it, she mentioned that her work schedule hadn't changed at all since we first met.

Sarah had simply come up against a new level of resistance, and had automatically selected the explanation for her overeating that sounded the most plausible.

A justification such as this is just like any other obstacle: if you don't see it, it's likely you'll trip over it and fall. All you need to do is to get better at noticing your justifications and identifying them for what they are. Then, you can either use the justification to overeat or you can let it go. You can let it go in one of two ways:

a) by seeing that the justification is false, as Sarah did, and not use it, or

b) by seeing that it does contain truth - for example, 'yes, eating addictively does seem to comfort me' - but still choosing not to use it as a reason to overeat.

• *A process of breaking specific patterns of addictive eating.* Taking control of any addiction requires going through a process of withdrawal. With most addictions the behaviour is stopped completely and the addict is almost immediately faced with this most difficult phase of recovery. How they cope with that withdrawal - especially the mental side - determines their long term success.

With eating, of course, you don't stop doing it entirely. Instead, you go through a series of mini-withdrawals associated with particular foods and particular circumstances. Let's say for example, you decide you want to stop eating chocolate after lunch every day, so you make a Plan for lunch leaving out the chocolate. Then, when you finish lunch, you desire your familiar dessert and feel empty and a bit lost without it. You're in conflict about what choice to make and struggle to identify your motivation while you reevaluate your priorities. At this point you are in withdrawal from food addiction.

This is how you change addictive behaviour. Just like any other addict, *you need to go through the experience of withdrawal in order to break free* - only with addictive eating, it doesn't happen all at once, it happens in bits and pieces.

In time, your addictive desire associated with that situation will fade, provided you are not reinforcing it by satisfying it with anything else, and provided you are genuinely choosing to accept it. Just like a fire, the desire burns itself out when you stop feeding it. (Take note that if you are very keen for it to fade, you're not fully accepting it).

Also, you may at times create new addictive patterns. You will see that whenever you do some addictive eating, your addictive desire will become reinforced, just as it would if you started smoking or taking any other addictive substance. If you started smoking now you would need to go through a withdrawal later on in order to stop. This means you'd feel a strong desire to smoke, needing to resolve your conflict about that in order to return to your level of control.

When it comes to addictive eating, all you need to do is to consistently break more patterns than you create new ones.

- *A process of discovering your limits to control.* With most other addictions, people are either completely out of control of their addictive behaviour or completely abstinent. Smokers, for example, either smoke all day, every day, or they don't smoke at all. Many try to compromise, but find that the odd cigarette here and there is impossible to maintain.

 You will find this 'all or none' principle applies to overeating too, to some extent, but only to some extent, *and the extent to which it does apply will be unique to you.*

 You probably know what your limits to control actually are. For example, you may know you are making an 'all or none' decision when you open a bag of crisps or when you buy a packet of Hobnobs. You may find that one bite before your Time sends you completely out of control of your eating for a week. Or a taste of sugar sends you off on a cookie binge. It's crucial that you tell the truth to yourself about this when you are making your choices, and it will almost certainly be considerably easier for you not to take the first bite in the first place.

Taking bites before your Time or after your Plan might not seem much of a problem at first, but it will erode the significance of the technique until you don't really have a technique at all. You may need to experience this a few times before you understand this.

In time, as you work with this technique, you'll probably find that your limits to control do change. For example, you could find that you've gained a degree of control that enables you to eat only half a packet of crisps (assuming it's something you want to do).

- *A process of developing your motivation.* It's inevitable you'll go through periods of time when your weight matters less to you and other times when it becomes very important. Whenever your weight becomes more significant to you - and this could be because you haven't lost any or because you have - you may react by eating more. If you experience big variations in both the quality and quantity of what you eat, that you are bingeing on junk food one day, nibbling on celery the next, this is usually the result of weight loss as a primary goal.

It may take a while for you to put your goal of weight loss into a different perspective, so that it's not the *only* thing you're after. This means that to begin with you may find it difficult to connect with reasons other than weight to accept your feelings of desire, so your motivation may not be as strong and effective as it could be. Remember that a preoccupation with appearance (i.e. other people's opinions of you) will blind you to the more private and personal rewards of taking control.

While you are out of control, though, one thing you can discover for yourself is that being in control of your eating has greater value to you than just losing weight. You may need to be out of control a lot before you can really appreciate this. Keep observing the difference in the quality of your life in any way other than your weight, developing greater interest in any motivation that has to do with your health and self-esteem. (1)

- *A process of changing your definition of 'hitting bottom'.* Many sober alcoholics go through an experience which becomes a turning point, a time when they say: 'Enough is enough!' and from that point on begin the process of sobering up. That turning point may have been a time when a career was destroyed, a relationship ended or even a time when their life was in danger because of

A PLAN FOR SUCCESS

Success and failure are seen in terms of weight.

'Whenever I think about eating or not eating something, my weight, shape and size are all that really matter.'

+

Fears that permission to overeat will lead to overeating, so thinks in terms of 'no choice' in order not to eat.

'I mustn't eat any more! If I say I'm free to overeat, I'm sure I will.'

+

Addictive desire to eat is either repressed or feels overwhelming.

'Eating less is easy for a while, but doesn't last. At some point I feel as if I've been possessed by something and I'm driven to overeat.'

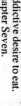

SOLUTIONS:

- Focus on motivation that has to do with anything other than the weight, size and shape of your body.
- See Chapters Two, Three and Four.

- Take responsibility by recognising you always have the freedom to eat anything you want.
- See Chapter Six.

- Set Times and make Plans. Use the Outine as much as you can in order to develop a positive response to your addictive desire to eat.
- See Chapter Seven.

RESULTS:

GENUINE, MAINTAINABLE CONTROL OVER ADDICTIVE OVEREATING: SELF-ESTEEM, CONFIDENCE, FREEDOM, FLEXIBILITY, LOSS OF BODY FAT, HEALTH, VITALITY AND ENERGY.

their drinking. The cost of the addiction had simply become too great and the alcoholic begins to consider that there must be a better way to live than this, that satisfying their addictive desire may not be worth it any more.

This turning point is called 'hitting bottom', and it's often regarded as an essential part of successful recovery. Overeating, of course, doesn't lead to quite such dramatic events as alcoholism does, but the same principle applies.

Every overeater will have a different personal definition of 'hitting bottom', but it's usually to do with weight. Your idea of 'hitting bottom' may be when you can't fit into a particular outfit, or when the scales reach a number you regard as significant. It's also possible that you have never hit your own 'bottom' and may not even have any clear idea of what that might be.

The crucial thing to understand here is that *you* are the one who decides when you will say: 'Enough is enough!' *You* are the one who determines what 'hitting bottom' for *you* actually is - and even whether you'll have one in the first place. Will it be your first heart attack? Or when you are diagnosed as diabetic? Or what?

My suggestion is to change your standards. Then, whenever you start to overeat, you can get back in control faster by refusing to put up with the consequences. Raise your standards, especially in any area other than your appearance. Remind yourself that your eating *matters*, that the quality of your life matters and that you matter. When I've eaten addictively, I've experienced my energy and my self-esteem drop, long before I put on any noticeable amount of weight. Observe this for yourself, make it matter to you, and there's your motivation to get back on track faster.

• *A natural process of ups and downs.* It's inevitable there will be times when you have unexpected insights and breakthroughs, when you find you are able to make changes in your eating you never thought possible. It's also likely that times like this will be followed by periods when nothing seems to change at all. This too is to be expected, and there's nothing wrong with it. It's only a problem if you take it as evidence that either the technique is useless or that you are useless and incapable of using it.

Be patient with yourself. Staying at one level could simply mean you are ready to move on to the next. Perhaps you've made some changes and then you settled for an eating style which is an improvement but you know it's still settling for something that's second rate, and that there's still plenty of room for improvement. What could be your next challenge?

TOLERATING IMPERFECTION

It will help you a great deal to give up any ideas you may have of doing this perfectly. Nobody can stay in control of addictive eating *perfectly*. For one thing, there is no such thing as a perfect definition of addictive eating, and there never will be. You can only say whether or not you eat addictively in terms of degree: either 'a great deal' or 'not very much' or somewhere in between. It is, by its very nature, imperfect.

Aspiring to perfection is going to get in your way. If you think perfection is a realistic goal, then no matter what you accomplish, you focus on the one thing 'wrong' and it's all cancelled out, it's all meaningless.

Perfectionism may attract you because you think it will bring you security, that if you use the technique perfectly, you'll be sure to stay in control. The truth is that you could use these techniques absolutely to the letter for any period of time, and then start to do a lot of overeating, completely out of control. Why? *Because it's not perfection that leads you to succeed in the long term; it's gaining an acceptance of your addictive desire to eat.* When you have achieved that to a significant extent, then, even when you do eat addictively, you can get back into control by accepting your desire.

Think of your addictive desire to eat as the payment you make in order to be in control. Do you prefer to be in control of your overeating? Then this is what it costs. It costs you moments of discomfort. If you make this payment, control of your addictive eating is yours to enjoy. If you don't make the payment, you lose it. I'm not referring to money, just moments of discomfort, while you feel your addictive desire.

The good news is that even if you are not perfect, you can always make progress. Even half-way through a binge, if you can see the value of stopping right there and if you then make a choice to accept your feeling of desire, that's *something*.

You will go out of control. All you need to do is get up one more time than you fall down. You will make mistakes. Who ever learned anything in their lives without making one single mistake? All you need to do is notice them, forgive yourself, and learn from them.

This requires courage, because you are trying to do something that is extremely important to you, so any amount of failure will cause you to suffer. The 'safe' solution is not to try in the first place, or not to try too hard - but then nothing changes.

In the past when I've been struggling with all this, I've often found it's precisely those times when I've felt the most hopeless that I am closest to a real breakthrough. The solution is right there in the problem, and all it usually takes is one or two very simple things to turn it around. All you need to do is to set yourself a Time, and then make present-time choices either to satisfy and reinforce your addictive desire to eat or to accept these addictive thoughts and feelings in order to gain the benefits you want.

When I'm in control of my eating I feel on top of the world, like there's nothing I can't do. All I need to do is pay the appropriate fee: an uncomfortable feeling of addictive desire. No, it's not easy and it's not magic - *but it works*!

WHAT PEOPLE SAY ABOUT *EATING LESS*

"Really feeling my addictive desire to eat - that awful, tense longing and excitement - is very uncomfortable, but somehow it makes me feel more whole, as if I have regained a part of myself which I have been drowning in food, or diets, for years.

I'm finding your warning to tolerate imperfection very helpful. I'm really dismayed at the thought that I may go out of control again, but have to recognise the wisdom of it!"

HELEN

Taking Control

1. Set a Time if you don't already have one. 'I'll start again tomorrow' is just another way to justify addictive eating in the present time. If you don't set a Time now, you're even less likely to do it tomorrow.

2. Keep this book around you and read it again from time to time, perhaps just dipping in to a few pages or chapters.
   As you think more about these concepts, and especially when you use the technique a bit, coming back to the book will enable you to own it more and make it more meaningful.

REFERENCES

Chapter 1

1. These recommendations are reported in the *American Journal of Clinical Nutrition* (1996; 63;474S-7S). A great number of studies substantiate this; one of the most significant is the Nurses Health Study, conducted by Harvard University researchers and published in *The New England Journal of Medicine* (1995; 333, 677-685). This study followed 115,195 women over 16 years and concludes:

   "Body weight and mortality from all causes were directly related among these middle-aged women. Lean women did not have excess mortality."

   To find your body mass index, divide your weight in kilos by the square of your height in meters. For example, let's say your height is 1.6 meters, so the square of that (1.6 x 1.6) is 2.56. Let's say your weight is 67.6 kilos. 67.6 divided by 2.56 is 26, so 26 is your BMI. A BMI of 25 and over is considered overweight and 30 obese.

2. Dr Andrew Prentice, Director of the Medical Research Council Dunn Clinical Nutrition Centre writes:

   "Physiological studies show that human metabolism is very poorly adapted to recognise excess fat consumption." (*British Medical Bulletin* 1997; 53, 229-237).

CHAPTER 2

1. *"...your problem is not excess weight so much as it is excess body fat coupled with too little muscle... it's imperative that you look beyond the simplistic notion of losing weight ... and concentrate on building muscle at the expense of fat."* From *Biomarkers: The 10 Keys to Prolong Vitality* by Drs William Evans and Irwin Rosenberg of Tufts University Department of Nutrition and Medicine, USA (Simon & Schuster).

   The interesting point here is that muscle weighs considerably more than fat. A body-builder, for example, will weigh more but carry less fat than their BMI would suggest.

2. *The Anorexia Nervosa Reference Book* by Roger Slade includes the following as part of a definition of the condition:

   "Steadfast and overriding, though often denied, preoccupation with first pursuing a low body weight and then maintaining it...' and *'To safeguard herself against what (she) calls 'losing control' - meaning not being able to stop eating - she strives to remain abnormally thin."*

CHAPTER 3

1. In *Make The Connection*, (Century) Oprah Winfrey and Bob Greene have written a beautiful passage about this which explains their title. Unfortunately, these few sentences are overshadowed by a preoccupation with weight loss for the rest of the book:

   "The connection is a change in perception. It is first realising that losing weight is not what is most important. Instead, the excess weight is merely a symptom of a larger problem and losing weight is a side effect, a nice one certainly, of something much more important. It is really about increasing self-confidence, inner strength, and discipline. It is about feeling better on a daily basis, having control over your life, and caring about yourself. Ultimately it is about self-love.

   (When you've made the connection) you will want only the best for you, which means exercising and eating right, as well as dealing with your problems in a healthy way. You will know you've made the connection when you care enough about yourself that you don't consider doing anything outside your best interest."

CHAPTER 4

1. *"Possibly the greatest misconception people have about the process of aging is that it's synonymous with illness. ... There are two principal factors responsible for the onset and severity of most chronic and degenerative conditions - your genetic heritage, which you cannot control; and your lifestyle, which you can and should control.*

   The goal of our program is to maintain vitality into old age. It grew out of the realisation that there are specific types of exercise and eating patterns that can greatly diminish the chances that people will develop a chronic disease; or if they're already suffering from one, could help them escape from the imprisonment of its debilitating symptoms." From *Biomarkers: The 10 Keys to Prolong Vitality* by Drs William Evans and Irwin Rosenberg of the Tufts University Department of Nutrition and Medicine, USA (Simon & Schuster).

CHAPTER 5

1. In his book *Timeless Healing: The Power and Biology of Belief*, Dr Herbert Benson, President of the Harvard Medical School's Mind/Body Medical Institute, describes phantom pregnancy (called 'pseudocyesis') in which physical changes are created by the mind:

   "In this condition, menstruation stops and abdominal swelling occurs at a rate similar to that of a normal pregnancy. Breasts grow larger and more tender, and nipples change pigment as is consistent with pregnancy. Nipples also increase in size and milk is secreted. Some

women feel what they think is fetal movement during the fourth or fifth month of a false pregnancy."

If a desire for a baby can produce all that, surely an addictive desire for food can create a physical sensation of hunger!

2. This study is referred to in *The Zone* by Barry Sears, Ph.D. (HarperCollins)

3. A major study of the eating habits of 11,000 people over a period of 17 years revealed a significant link between a longer, healthier life and the consumption of fruit. No other food was found to have such a significant effect. Regular fruit eaters had a 24% reduction in death from heart disease, a 32% reduction in deaths from strokes and a 21% reduction in deaths from other causes. Reported in the *British Medical Journal* (1996; 313: 755-779).

4. If my experience with clients is anything to go by, a great many people are not fully aware of the effect food has on their health. An article in *The Independent* (July 24, 1997) reported the findings of the National Heart Forum, that Britain has the worst heart disease death rates in the Western world:

   "Heart attacks do not come out of the blue. More than 90 per cent of them have at least one factor - raised blood pressure, raised cholesterol or smoking - which at least doubles the risk. ... The average diet is a disaster and the average level of physical activity is totally inadequate. We need to make dramatic changes, not just fiddle around the edges."

5. A number of writers on health and nutrition speak of the positive effect eating less has on our health. Leslie Kenton, in her book *The New Ultrahealth,* refers to a number of different studies which support this, including the following:

   "Dr Alexander Leaf from Harvard Medical School, spent several years studying three cultures where the people were exceptionally long-lived... but who at the same time showed few signs of degenerative changes traditionally associated with age... They suffered neither tooth decay, heart disease, mental illness, obesity nor cancer... they led extremely active lives, regardless of their age, and had vigorous sex lives well into their eighties and nineties... They ate a very low-calorie diet. While the average Briton or American eats somewhere between 3,000 and 3,500 calories a day ... they ate a mere 1,700... low in fats and in proteins from animal sources and high in fresh foods, a great many of them eaten raw... they had never heard of sugar..."

   Barry Sears puts it quite simply in *The Zone*: *"...the best way to retard aging is to restrict calories, but not essential nutrients."*

   And in *The Optimum Nutrition Bible,* (Piatkus) Patrick Holford states:

*"It is more than likely that the leaner you are the longer you will live...
It is about giving your body exactly what it needs and no more."*

CHAPTER 6

1. Stanford University neuroscientist and stress expert Robert Sapolsky describes a number of experiments that show how stress increases when we have no choice - or even when we just think we have no choice:
   "This is an extraordinarily powerful variable in modulating the stress-response... the exercise of choice is not critical; rather it is the belief that you have it." From *Why Zebras Don't Get Ulcers* (WH Freeman)

2. Of course, if you are in some kind of treatment programme, perhaps even hospitalised, this loss of personal responsibility is quite real:
   "Patients in our own clinic often comment on the security provided by the treatment, and data that we have collected during weight loss programmes showed that craving and the sense of loss of control goes down and not up during the active phase of treatment." However this report goes on to say, *"most weight control treatments induce weight cycles... a series of patients were reduced to normal weight in a hospital programme. By the four year follow-up almost 60% of the patients were close to their initial weight with over one third having exceeded it."* International Journal of Obesity (1996; 20, S1-S8).

3. An excellent book which deals in detail with this aspect of addictive behaviour is: *Codependent No More: How to stop controlling others and start caring for yourself* by Melody Beattie, published by Harper Collins, A Hazeldon Book.

4. The value of delayed gratification is explored in *Emotional Intelligence* by Daniel Goleman, Ph.D in which the author states: *"There is perhaps no psychological skill more fundamental than resisting impulse."*

CHAPTER 7

1. From the *New Scientist,* October 1, 1994:
   "These cues are very powerful - videos of drug paraphernalia cause changes in brain chemistry and skin temperature in addicts. And they are also very hard to avoid."

2. In *The Six Pillars of Self-Esteem*, Nathaniel Branden writes about the value and practice of acceptance:
   "When we fight a block it grows stronger. When we acknowledge, experience and accept it, it begins to melt because its continued existence requires opposition."
   And:
   "To 'accept' is more than simply to 'acknowledge' or 'admit'. It is to experience, stand in the presence of, contemplate the reality of, absorb

into my consciousness. I need to open myself to and fully experience unwanted emotions, not just perfunctorily recognise them."

CHAPTER 8

1. *"All joint problems, such as arthritis, are produced by acidity in the body. This acidity can be caused by high intakes of antibiotics or sugar, or incompletely digested food. ... Rheumatism, too, has acidity at its root, as do frozen shoulder, tennis elbow, lumbago or back pain."* From *Gut Reaction* by Gudrun Jonsson (Vermilion).

CHAPTER 9

1. The Women's Nutritional Advisory Service has been providing help for women for over a decade and has an 85% success rate in reducing symptoms of PMS. Nutritionist Maryon Stewart, who set up the Service, has written a book called *No More PMS* (Vermilion).

2. See Reference 2, Chapter 5.

3. *"...considerable inaccuracy in self-reports of energy intake has been documented. ...Because the degree of underreporting increases with intake, it is speculated that individuals tend to report intakes that are closer to perceived norms than to actual intake."* Nutritional Reviews (1990; 48/10, 373-379).
   "Whereas many people underreport their calorie intake, the degree of underreporting is greater in obese subjects." The New England Journal of Medicine (1992; 327, 1893-1898).

4. Dr Andrew Prentice of the Medical Research Council Dunn Nutrition Centre writes:
   "...energy balance only needs to be displaced by a tiny fraction for the cumulative effects to result in obesity. The fattest man in the world died recently in his mid-forties weighing 465kg (73 stone). Even this enormous accumulation of fat required an excess equivalent to only a small bar of chocolate each day. ... human metabolism is very poorly adapted to recognise excess fat consumption and to reestablish fat balance." British Medical Bulletin (1997; 53,229-237)

5. According to Daniel Goleman in *Emotional Intelligence*, one of the most thorough studies of eating disorders, conducted with over 900 girls, identified 'a failure to tell distressing feelings from one another and to control them' as a key factor. He goes on to say:
   "Some obese people are unable to tell the difference between being scared, angry, and hungry, and so lump all those feelings together as signifying hunger, which leads them to overeat whenever they feel upset."

6. *"There are many nutritionally related causes of depression, the most common being sub-optimum nutrition resulting in poor mental and*

physical energy." From *The Optimum Nutrition Bible.* Patrick Holford's book *"Mental Health/Mental Illness: The Nutrition Connection"* is well worth looking into on this subject.

7. '£11M lotto hulk binges to death' reported in *The Sun,* December 31, 1996.

CHAPTER 10

1. There's quite a bit of research which casts doubt on the notion that biochemistry causes addictive behaviour. For example, 50 subjects who suffered from 'binge eating disorder' were recruited for a trial and given a placebo for 4 weeks before they went on to the active medication which was being evaluated. Binge eating fell by an average of 72% (from 6 to 1.7 binge episodes per week) during the placebo period. 22 of the 50 became ineligible for the trial because they were no longer experiencing the required disorder. *International Journal of Obesity* (1996:20, 1-6).

   Similar results show up in research on other addictions which are commonly thought of as physical:

   "Alcoholics were asked to indicate their desire for alcohol after drinking a drink containing one ounce of 100 proof vodka. The alcohol taste in the drink was disguised and only one-half of the subjects were informed that the drink contained alcohol. Only those subjects who were aware that they consumed alcohol reported significant cravings to drink further. Subjects who ingested the identical amount of alcohol, but who were not informed of its alcohol content reported no cravings. This demonstration, as well as others, indicates that craving depends as much upon one's cognitions as on one's physiological or pharmacological experiences." Appetite (1990; 15, 231-246).

   In another experiment, smokers were asked to refrain from smoking for 12 hours. Then half the group were given ordinary cigarettes to smoke and the rest smoked cigarettes which looked the same, but in which the nicotine - the active drug - had been removed. *"The regular and de-nicotinized cigarettes were equivalent in reducing acute withdrawal symptoms."* Pharmacology, Biochemistry and Behaviour (1995; 50, 91-96).

2. Dr Paul Rozin of the University of Pennsylvania isolated the active ingredient in chocolate - theobromine - and fed it to volunteers in the form of pills. The pills didn't satisfy their craving and Dr Rozin concluded:

   "People like chocolate because it tastes good. It has nothing to do with the pharmacological effects." Reported in *The Daily Telegraph,* (February 14, 1998).

3. Overweight volunteers who claim to be unable to lose weight, no matter what they eat, were studied at the Obesity Research Centre at Columbia

University. The researchers concluded:

"The failure of some obese subjects to lose weight while eating a diet they report as low in calories is due to an energy intake substantially higher than reported and an overestimation of physical activity." The *New England Journal of Medicine* (1992; 327, 1893-1898).

4. *"...an average 70-year-old person needs 500 fewer calories per day to maintain his or her body weight than an average 25-year-old. The average 80-year-old needs 600 fewer calories. In short, from around age 20 onward, you need to take in about 100 calories per day less each decade to maintain the status quo."* From *Biomarkers: The Ten Keys to Prolonging Vitality* by Evans and Rosenberg (Simon & Schuster).

5. *"The increases in obesity seen in many Western countries over the past few decades, and the even larger increases in some of the Pacific Islanders whose countries have undergone dramatic lifestyle changes, are not reflections of genetic changes, but of gene expression facilitated by the environment. The most widely held view is that genes confer a susceptibility or predisposition to obesity and genetically predisposed individuals may be especially susceptible to aspects of lifestyle such as low activity and high fat diets, and gain weight more readily."* *International Journal of Obesity* (1996;20, S1-S8).

CHAPTER 11

1. Whether you are a smoker or an ex-smoker, my book *How To Stop Smoking And Stay Stopped For Good,* (Vermilion) will show you how to deal with your addictive desire to smoke.

2. This information on appetite suppressants was taken from an article which appeared in *Time* magazine on September 23, 1996. *The New England Journal of Medicine* (August 28, 1997) published an editorial on diet pills which included the following passages:

"It has never been shown, and it is highly implausible, that appetite-suppressant drugs can maintain weight loss indefinitely. To date, studies of these drugs have demonstrated efficacy only for short-term weight loss. Their safety if taken over a period of many years is doubtful, since the risk of serious toxicity appears to increase with the duration of use."

"The medical community should be sceptical of quick pharmacologic fixes for obesity and should continue to support the view that alterations in diet and physical activity - though difficult to implement and sustain - will always be central components of prevention and treatment."

3. An excellent book on the difference between healthy and unhealthy guilt, and how to heal the latter, is: *Guilt Is The Teacher, Love Is The Lesson* by Joan Borysenko (HarperCollins)

CHAPTER 12

1. It's often said that people eat commercially prepared 'junk' food because it's less expensive, but in terms of nutritional value, you are much better off with food closer to its natural state. As a general principle, the more stages of processing a product has gone through - milling, chopping, cooking, designing, packaging, marketing - all of which costs money, the less nutritional value you'll get for your money. Notice that those cultures in our world today which have the most overweight populations are also the most affluent.

   Eating quantities of cheap, processed foods to 'fill yourself up' is doing little more than satisfying your addictive desire. Feeding most addictions is an expensive business, and food addiction can be one of the most costly to maintain.

2. *"Flour, rice and sugar loses more than 77 per cent of their zinc, chromium and manganese in the refining process. Other essential nutrients, such as essential fats, will not be present in processed foods..."* From *The Optimum Nutrition Bible*.

   Much of the most recent advice on nutrition warns us against eating wheat in any form, suggesting we reduce our consumption and even eliminate it entirely, at least for a while to see if our health improves. It is certainly eaten too much as it's found in most prepared foods, and of course bread, pasta, pies, quiches, biscuits, pastries and cakes.

3. *"Taking large amounts of unsaturated fatty acids without extra vitamin E will quickly use up the body's supply of the vitamin."* From *Free Radicals and Disease Prevention* by David Lin.

   "Refining and processing vegetable oils can change the nature of the polyunsaturated oil. (Margarine, for example) blocks the body's ability to use healthy polyunsaturated oils." From *The Optimum Nutrition Bible* by Patrick Holford.

4. *"Eating in a healthy fashion doesn't have to be complicated. In general, just try to eat more fresh vegetables, fruits, cereals and legumes. Limit your consumption of red meats and cold cuts, substituting poultry without skin and fish as often as possible. Avoid fried and other fatty foods. And substitute low- or non-fat dairy products for their whole-milk counterparts."* From *Biomarkers: The 10 Keys to Prolong Vitality* by Drs William Evans and Irwin Rosenberg of Tufts University Department of Nutrition and Medicine, USA (Simon & Schuster).

   Regarding two recent reports on nutrition, one from the World Cancer Research Fund and the other by the British Committee on the Medical Aspects of Food and Nutrition Policy:

   "Both reports emphasise the importance of increasing intake of fibre and of fruits and vegetables to five or more servings a day. They also